Lab Manual

chemistry

FIFTH EDITION

bju press

Greenville, South Carolina

The writers and publisher have made every effort to ensure that the laboratory exercises in this publication are safe when conducted according to the instructions provided. We assume no responsibility for any injury or damage caused or sustained while performing activities in this book. Conventional and homeschool teachers, parents, and guardians should closely supervise students who perform the exercises in this manual. More specific safety information is contained in the CHEMISTRY Teacher Lab Manual Fifth Edition, published by BJU Press. Therefore, it is highly recommended that the Teacher Lab Manual be used in conjunction with this manual.

NOTE: The fact that materials produced by other publishers may be referred to in this volume does not constitute an endorsement of the content or theological position of materials produced by such publishers. Any references and ancillary materials are listed as an aid to the student or the teacher and in an attempt to maintain the accepted academic standards of the publishing industry.

CHEMISTRY Student Lab Manual
Fifth Edition

Coordinating Writer
David M. Quigley, MEd

Writers
Christopher D. Coyle
Kelly Driskell

Biblical Worldview
Renton Rathbun, ThM

Academic Oversight
Jeff Heath, EdD
Rachel Santopietro, MEd

Editor
Rick Vasso, MDiv

Cover, Design, and Interior Concept Design
Sarah Lompe

Page Layout
Carrie Walker

Illustrator
Ina Stanimirova
    c/o Lemonadeillustration agency

Permissions
Kathryn Jackson
Elizabeth Walker

Project Coordinators
Heather Chisholm
Chris Daniels

Photo credits appear on pages 246–47.

The text for this book is set in Adobe Minion Pro, Adobe Myriad Pro, Arial by Monotype Typography, Helvetica, Minion Math by Typoma GmbH, Playfair Display by Claus Eggers Sørensen, Raleway, and STIX.

The cover photo shows a close-up of a cluster of bubbles on a black background.

© 2021 BJU Press
Greenville, South Carolina 29609
Fourth Edition © 2015 BJU Press
Originally published as *Laboratory Manual: Chemistry* © 1985 BJU Press

Printed in the United States of America

ISBN 978-1-62856-688-8

15 14 13 12 11 10 9 8 7 6 5 4 3 2 1

Contents

Welcome to the Laboratory!   *vi*

01 FOUNDATIONS OF CHEMISTRY

1A **The Great Biscuit Bake-Off**
Relating the Composition and Properties of Biscuits   1

1B **The Safety Saga** Thinking Safe in the Laboratory   5

02 MATTER

2A **Needle in a Haystack** Separating Mixtures   9

2B **Zebroids, Wolphins, and Ligers, Oh My!** Classifying Matter   15

03 MEASUREMENTS IN CHEMISTRY

3A **Metric Unicorns** Exploring the Metric System   19

3B **You Are My Density** Inquiring into Measurement   23

04 ATOMIC STRUCTURE

4   **All That Glitters Is Not Copper-63**
Investigating Mixtures of Isotopes   25

05 ELECTRON ARRANGEMENT

5A **Bulls-Eye!** Modeling an Atomic Orbital   33

5B **Seeing Light in a New Way** Exploring Spectroscopy   37

06 PERIODIC TABLE AND ELEMENTS

6A **Exposed to the Elements** Inquiring into Properties of Elements   45

6B **An Elemental Merry-Go-Round** Exploring Periodic Trends   47

07 CHEMICAL BONDS

7A **The Name's Bond—Covalent Bond** Modeling Covalent Bonds   53

7B **Bulletproof Chemistry**
Relating Chemical Bonds and Physical Properties   59

08 BOND THEORIES AND MOLECULAR GEOMETRY

8A **The Shape of Things** Modeling Molecules   65

8B **Change of Address** Investigating Molecular Orbitals   71

09 CHEMICAL COMPOUNDS

9   **Compounds Scavenger Hunt** Naming Chemical Compounds   79

Contents

10 CHEMICAL REACTIONS AND EQUATIONS

10A **Expeditions in Chemical Equations**
Investigating Chemical Reactions and Equations ... 87

10B **With a Chance of Precipitation** Inquiring into Solubility ... 91

11 CHEMICAL CALCULATIONS

11A **Torching Metals** Determining Empirical Formulas ... 95

11B **Chymestry** Using Stoichiometric Relationships ... 101

12 GASES

12A **Cold and Calculating** Finding Absolute Zero ... 107

12B **An Aquanaut's World** Predicting the Production of Oxygen ... 111

13 SOLIDS AND LIQUIDS

13A **Cracking the Crystal** Relating Geology to Chemistry ... 119

13B **Forces of Nature** Exploring Intermolecular Forces in Liquids ... 123

14 SOLUTIONS

14A **One Giant Solution** Making a Solubility Curve ... 133

14B **Sugar, Sugar** Determining the Sugar Content in Beverages ... 137

15 THERMOCHEMISTRY

15A **Hot Shot** Finding the Specific Heat of a Metal ... 143

15B **No Anchovies, Please!**
Exploring Enthalpies of Solution and Reaction ... 149

16 CHEMICAL KINETICS

16A **Chemistry—A Contact Sport?**
Exploring Concentration's Effect on Reaction Rates ... 157

16B **Don't Overreact** Determining a Rate Law ... 163

17 CHEMICAL EQUILIBRIUM

17A **Stressed Out** Inquiring into Le Châtelier's Principle ... 169

17B **Precipitous Changes** Exploring Solubility Products ... 171

18 ACIDS, BASES, AND SALTS

18A **Colorful Chemistry** Exploring Acid-Base Indicators ... 175

18B **Say Cheese!** Measuring Concentration by Titration ... 181

Contents

19 OXIDATION AND REDUCTION

19A **The Dead, Twitching Frog Mystery** Investigating a Voltaic Cell   *187*

19B **Essential Medicine** Using Redox Titration   *193*

20 ORGANIC CHEMISTRY

20A **Makes Scents!** Synthesizing Esters   *199*

20B **Squeaky Clean** Investigating Soaps and Detergents   *203*

21 BIOCHEMISTRY

21A **Balancing Act** Testing Macronutrients in Food   *207*

21B **The Proof Is in the Jell-O®** Investigating Enzymes   *213*

22 NUCLEAR CHEMISTRY

22A **It's Only a Matter of Time** Investigating Half-Life   *217*

22B **Atomic Asteroids**
Determining Mass Defect and Binding Energy   *225*

APPENDIX

A **Laboratory Safety and First-Aid Rules**   *231*

B **Laboratory Equipment**   *233*

C **Laboratory Techniques**   *236*

D **Graphing Techniques**   *240*

E **Writing Formal Lab Reports**   *242*

PERIODIC TABLE OF THE ELEMENTS   *252*

Welcome to the Laboratory!

A chemistry laboratory is anything but boring. Laboratories are places where exciting discoveries are made, old ideas are challenged, and new ideas are formed. But a laboratory can't do any of those exciting things on its own. It needs a chemist. ***THAT'S YOU!***

Thinking like a Chemist

Who, me? Yes, you!

"But I'm just a high-school chemistry student!"

But you can be a student chemist! Even if you don't see a science career in your future, you can develop skills this year to help you work like a chemist at your own level. You'll learn to think like a scientist—being safe in the laboratory, making predictions, collecting data, and testing your ideas. Sometimes you'll have to think about how to solve a problem on your own, without any procedures spelled out in the lab activity. These lab activities will have the word *inquiring* in the subtitle. You'll learn how to collect data with the equipment that you have to work with and how to tell whether the data that you've collected is good. The equipment for these activities can come in different shapes and sizes, both high-tech and low-tech. You'll learn to use chemicals, laboratory burners, and good old-fashioned glassware. But you'll also use the internet, possibly probeware, and maybe even your smartphone.

Above all, learn to do science within the framework of a Christian worldview. Everyone has a worldview. It is the lens through which you view everything. A Christian gains his worldview from the Bible. This worldview doesn't just affect what he believes about God, Jesus, and salvation—it also affects how he views science, history, and even how he interacts with other people.

As a student scientist, keep your worldview in mind. When you do an experiment, think about how it relates to a biblical worldview. And you're not just a student chemist. You're a Christian student chemist. As a Christian student chemist, you are interpreting the world as God has already interpreted it in His Word. Christians should see science as an important gift of God, given to humans so that they can obey the Creation Mandate (Gen. 1:28) and the two great commandments (Matt. 22:37–40). When Christians do science, they bring glory to God and help their fellow humans to live in this fallen world. Therefore, some questions will specifically ask you to use your worldview to apply the information from your lab activity to a real-world problem. You will be challenged to consciously think like a Christian as you're doing science.

A Christian shouldn't see science as a pathway to truth. Rather, he should look to the Bible, the one source of absolute truth, to establish the guidelines and proper role of science in human life. Scientists working from a Christian worldview should evaluate existing scientific models in light of Scripture and challenge or revise them when they conflict. And as they create models of their own, they must test them for agreement with the revealed truths in the Bible. When we act in this way, we glorify God by using science as He intended.

But what good is all of this? Why is it important to develop the skills and mindset of a chemist? As a Christian, learn to see science as an amazing tool to glorify God and help people by obeying God's command to wisely use His creation. We should do the work of chemistry within the context of a Christian worldview and use it as God intended in ways that harmonize with His Word.

SO ...
let's get into the laboratory!

Keys to Laboratory Success

Lab activities can be both interesting and fun. But your laboratory experience largely depends on you. If you take these activities seriously, keep your brain engaged, and try to learn as much as possible, you'll come away from the laboratory feeling that your time has been well spent. On the other hand, if you treat lab activities carelessly, you probably won't learn much nor will you have a genuine sense of accomplishment. The following guidelines will help you get the most from lab activities. And they'll also help you experience the true pleasure of a brain at work.

1. Read through the entire lab procedure before class. You'll know what to expect, and you'll be far less likely to make mistakes or forget a crucial step.

2. Review the parts of your textbook that apply to the lab activity. Your teacher may give you specific review guidelines.

3. Come to class well prepared. Bring your textbook, calculator, paper, and pencil. You won't necessarily need all these for every lab activity, but you'll regret it if they're sitting in your locker on a day when you *do* need them!

4. Begin the lab activity only when instructed to do so by your teacher. Read each lab procedure step carefully so that you don't make foolish mistakes. Procedure steps are identified by lettered bullets (e.g., A, B, C). If you're ever in doubt about what to do, *ask*, don't guess.

5. Lab activity questions are mixed in with the procedure steps. They're identified by numbers (e.g., 1., 2., 3.).

6. Many lab activities require you to record data in tables. Typically data tables are located at the end of the activity.

7. Record your results from measurements and calculations carefully and accurately.

8. Most lab activity questions ask you to explain your answer. Don't view this requirement as pointless busywork. Explaining something makes you think more deeply about it. It also helps you connect principles from the textbook and class discussion to what you're doing in the laboratory.

9. Keep your laboratory area tidy. At the end of class, put away your equipment and dispose of trash according to your teacher's instructions.

10. While socializing may seem like a lot more fun than the lab activity, leave that behavior outside the laboratory door. You'll be more focused, get better results, and make far fewer mistakes.

Staying Safe

Nothing ruins a day quite so much as getting hurt in the laboratory. While the lab activities in this manual have been carefully designed to be safe, no lab activity is perfectly safe. For this reason, you should maintain constant vigilance when you're working through one. You should always use protective equipment when it's specified.

Rather than cover laboratory safety in this introduction, we've devoted an entire lab activity on the topic (Lab 1B—*The Safety Saga*). This lab activity isn't just a list of do's and don'ts. It takes a novel approach to safety, one that we hope will make laboratory safety more enjoyable and more effective. Be sure to give Lab 1B your full attention so that your class can have an accident-free year!

One of the most important safety precautions that you can take is to wear eye protection. Yes, goggles can be uncomfortable, but a little discomfort is better than losing an eye. *Always* wear your goggles anytime you are working with glassware, chemicals, or projectiles. For lab activities that require eye protection or other safety precautions, you will find the appropriate safety icons that pertain to that activity immediately below the activity's equipment list. The icons that you will see are listed below.

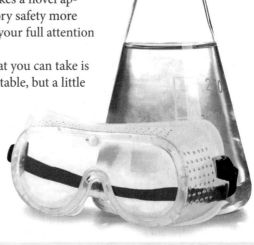

 Body Protection—Chemicals or other materials could damage your skin or clothing. You should wear a laboratory apron, chemical-resistant gloves, or both.

 Chemical Fumes—Chemical fumes may present a danger. Use a chemical fume hood or make sure that the area is well ventilated.

 Corrosive Substance—Acids and bases are corrosive substances that can cause damage to skin and eyes. Wear proper protective equipment and follow safe handling procedures.

 Electricity—An electrical device (e.g., hot plate, lamp, microscope) will be used. Use the device with care.

 Extreme Temperature—Extremely hot or cold temperatures may cause skin damage. Use proper tools to handle laboratory equipment.

 Eye Protection—There is a possible danger to the eyes from chemicals or other materials. Wear safety goggles.

 Fire Hazard—A heat source or open flame is used. Be careful to avoid skin burns and the ignition of combustible materials.

 Gas—Improper use of gas can result in burns, explosion, or suffocation. Be careful to check that the gas is turned off when you are finished.

 Sharp Object—Use care with the equipment in this lab activity to avoid cuts from sharp instruments or broken glassware.

 Toxic Material—A substance in the investigation could be poisonous if ingested.

Since some lab activities have specific steps with unique safety challenges, special safety notes are occasionally placed within the activity in ***bold italic font*** to emphasize their importance. For additional information on laboratory safety, see Appendix A.

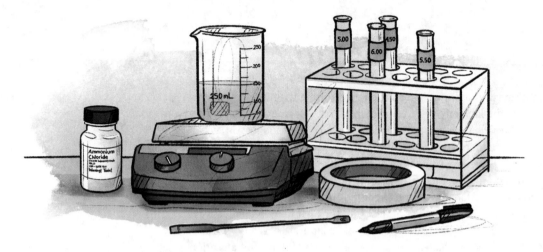

Lab Equipment and Techniques

Science involves both equipment and techniques that you may not be familiar with. To help, we have included appendixes for these. Appendix B is a visual glossary of laboratory equipment, and Appendix C explains many of the techniques that you will need for the lab activities in this manual.

Inquiry Lab Activities

As you work through this lab activity book, you will find inquiry lab activities. These activities are part of being a student scientist. Inquiry lab activities give you an opportunity to create your own activity about a given subject. You will ask questions, form hypotheses, design investigations, collect and analyze data, draw conclusions, communicate results, and often develop additional questions. These are tasks that scientists do every day.

Writing Formal Lab Reports

Communication is a key facet of science. Scientists need to communicate their findings to other scientists and ultimately to the world. Student scientists do this through writing formal lab reports, which you will write routinely if you take a college-level science course. Appendix E describes how to write a formal lab report. Use this to prepare your reports and to prepare for future science endeavors.

Let the Year Begin!

One of the pleasures that we get from writing this book is knowing that for many of you the laboratory will become a special place. We invite you to come into the laboratory part of this course expecting to learn new and fascinating things. Look forward to the challenge of getting your hands on science. Your visits to the laboratory could be life-changing for you.

WELCOME!

EQUIPMENT

- kitchen oven
- large bowl
- measuring cups
- measuring spoons
- pastry blender
- rolling pin
- biscuit cutter
- cookie sheets
- spatula
- flour
- sugar
- baking powder
- salt
- butter
- milk
- cream of tartar
- shortening
- eggs
- toppings for biscuits (optional)
- laboratory apron
- goggles

The Great Biscuit Bake-Off

Relating the Composition and Properties of Biscuits

Biscuits, or hardtack, have been known since ancient times. Because they were light, nutritious, and could keep for years if baked hard and stored dry, they were the food of choice for Roman legionnaires, British sailors, and Confederate and Union soldiers alike during the Civil War. Cooking involves chemistry, so baking biscuits is really applied chemistry. In fact, the study of chemistry may have begun with the science of food preparation. It is this chemistry of biscuit baking that you will explore today.

How do changes to the ratio of ingredients in a biscuit affect its properties?

You will be making three different biscuit recipes in a great biscuit bake-off to see which one you like the best. When you scan the list of ingredients and the procedures, you'll see that the recipes use similar ingredients and require baking at the same temperature for about the same length of time. But you will find that small variations in the recipes make a big difference in the taste and texture of the biscuits.

Salt (sodium chloride, NaCl) and sugar (sucrose, $C_{12}H_{22}O_{11}$) are chemicals that affect the taste of biscuits. Butter, milk, and shortening contain fats that affect their texture. Flour is the main ingredient—it binds the biscuit together and is what gives you energy when you enjoy one.

QUESTIONS

» How do I make scientific observations?

» How do the properties of foods change in response to a change in their ingredients?

» How are cooking and chemistry related?

One of the most important ingredients in biscuits is the *leavening agent*, or the chemical in biscuits that makes them rise. In all three recipes, baking powder is the leavening agent. Baking powder is a mixture of chemicals including baking soda (sodium bicarbonate or sodium hydrogen carbonate, $NaHCO_3$) and some kind of acid or acid salt that chemically reacts to produce carbon dioxide gas, similar to the typical homemade volcano that uses vinegar and baking soda. Baking soda, or sodium bicarbonate, will cause food to taste bitter if there is too much of it in a baked good. Baking powder often includes other substances such as calcium dihydrogen phosphate $[Ca(H_2PO_4)_2]$ and aluminum sodium bis(sulfate) $[NaAl(SO_4)_2]$. Eggs can also act as a leavening agent in baked goods when they are whipped. They also help combine the liquids in the recipe that don't normally mix together, such as oil and milk.

Procedure

RECIPE 1: BASIC BISCUITS

2 cups flour

1 teaspoon sugar

1 tablespoon baking powder

1 teaspoon salt

8 tablespoons butter, cubed

3/4 cup milk

A Preheat the oven to 425°. In a large bowl, combine the flour, sugar, baking powder, and salt.

B Using a pastry blender, cut the butter into the flour mixture until crumbly.

C Mix in milk until just moistened and turn onto a floured surface, kneading a little and rolling out to 3/4 inch thick. Cut with biscuit cutter.

D Place biscuits on a cookie sheet and bake for 10–12 minutes or until lightly browned.

RECIPE 2: BAKING POWDER BISCUITS

2 cups flour

2 tablespoons sugar

1 tablespoon baking powder

1/2 teaspoon salt

1/2 cup shortening

1 egg, beaten

2/3 cup milk

E Preheat the oven to 425°. In a large bowl, combine the flour, sugar, baking powder, and salt.

F Using a pastry blender, cut the shortening into the flour mixture until crumbly.

G Mix in milk and egg until just moistened, and turn onto a floured surface, kneading a little and rolling out to 3/4 inch thick. Cut with biscuit cutter.

H Place biscuits on a cookie sheet and bake for 10–12 minutes or until lightly browned.

RECIPE 3: DROP BISCUITS

2 cups flour

2 tablespoons sugar

1 tablespoon baking powder

1/2 teaspoon cream of tartar

1/4 teaspoon salt

1/2 cup melted butter

1 cup milk

I Preheat the oven to 425°. In a large bowl, combine the flour, sugar, baking powder, cream of tartar, and salt.

J Stir the melted butter and milk into the flour mixture until just moistened.

K Use a tablespoon to drop dollops of dough onto a cookie sheet. Bake for 10–12 minutes or until lightly browned.

Analysis

1. How do you think the biscuits that you made today differ from those used in historical times, as discussed in the introduction? You may need to do some research to answer this question.

   _____

   _____

2. Taste all three types of biscuits, either plain or with the same topping on each. Which one do you like the best? Explain why.

   _____

   _____

3. Why did Question 2 have you taste all three types of biscuits either plain or with the same topping on each?

   _____

   _____

4. Compare the ingredients of all three recipes. What do you notice that is different?

   _____

   _____

   _____

5. Compare the textures of all three biscuits. Is there one that is different from the others?

   _____

   _____

6. Cut apart a biscuit. Look at the holes in it. Where do you think the holes come from?

   _____

   _____

   The chemical reaction that occurs in the process of leavening is shown below.

$$NaAl(SO_4)_2\,(s) + 3\,NaHCO_3\,(s) \longrightarrow Al(OH)_3\,(s) + 2\,Na_2SO_4\,(s) + 3\,CO_2\,(g)$$

The first two chemicals—aluminum sodium bis(sulfate) and sodium hydrogen carbonate—are found in baking powder.

7. What do you think would happen if you added more baking soda (sodium hydrogen carbonate) to the biscuits without changing any other ingredients?

   _____

   _____

   _____

8. What do you think would happen if you added more baking soda (sodium hydrogen carbonate) than the aluminum sodium bis(sulfate) could react with?

_____

_____

_____

    One of the three recipes includes an ingredient called cream of tartar, which is the chemical potassium hydrogen tartrate, or potassium bitartrate ($KHC_4H_4O_6$). It is used in addition to the baking powder in your recipes and acts in a manner similar to aluminum sodium bis(sulfate).

9. Look at the reaction below Question 6 on page 3. If cream of tartar is an acid salt like aluminum sodium bis(sulfate), what is it likely to react with to form carbon dioxide gas? Where is this chemical coming from?

_____

_____

10. Suggest some other things that could affect the texture and taste of biscuits other than its ingredients.

_____

_____

_____

11. The milk in these recipes adds moisture to the biscuits because of its high water content. If there were a fourth recipe that had no milk in it, what do you think the texture would be like? Besides milk or water, do you think there is another ingredient that you could increase or decrease to account for the missing moisture?

_____

_____

_____

12. One of your classmates is allergic to milk. How could you modify one of these recipes so that he could eat these bicuits?

_____

_____

13. How does food science involve chemistry?

_____

_____

_____

Name _____

Date _____

EQUIPMENT

- digital camera, smartphone, or camcorder
- laboratory safety equipment
- chemical bottle with GHS label
- SDS

The Safety Saga

Thinking Safe in the Laboratory

Explosions! Fire! Flashes of color! These are what you want to see in the chemistry laboratory. But, we *don't* want them to happen in an uncontrolled way. Your teacher, administrator, and parents want you to explore chemistry safely. But safety is no fun, right? Wrong! *Getting hurt* is no fun. In this lab activity, you'll have some fun learning to "Think Safe."

How can I prevent accidents and injuries in the laboratory?

QUESTIONS

» What are safe and unsafe behaviors in the chemistry laboratory?

» What should I do if my lab partner gets injured?

» Where is the safety equipment in the chemistry laboratory?

» What information can I find on a GHS safety label?

» What information can I find on a Safety Data Sheet (SDS)?

The table below shows safety equipment that is often used in chemistry laboratories. Be sure that you can quickly and easily locate each piece of safety equipment in your laboratory.

Equipment	Purpose
eyewash station	removes chemicals that may splash into the eyes
shower	removes chemicals that may splash onto clothing; also, may be used to extinguish clothing fires
fire blanket	extinguishes clothing fires; extinguishes fires on the laboratory bench
fire extinguisher	extinguishes fires in the laboratory (different types of extinguishers for different kinds of fires)
first aid kit	provides basic medical supplies for treating common injuries

You will be taking some pictures and possibly creating some videos to teach the other students in your class safe laboratory behavior—a "Chemistry Safety Saga." To help you know what to do, see Appendix A on Laboratory Safety and First-Aid Rules and Appendix C on Laboratory Techniques to give you some hints on how to create your videos.

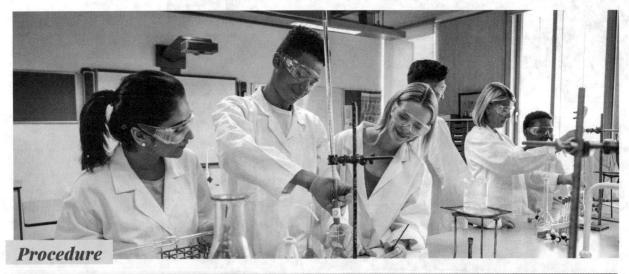

Procedure

THE SAFETY SAGA

Create videos or take pictures that teach your classmates the ten safe laboratory skills and behaviors listed below. Be sure to answer the questions! If you demonstrate safety equipment in your video or pictures, don't actually activate them; just pretend to. Don't forget the information in the appendixes! Have fun!

A What should I wear in the laboratory?

B How should I smell chemicals in the laboratory?

C How should I mix acid and water when called for in a lab activity?

D What are some examples of unsafe behavior in the laboratory? (Remember to make this video or picture in a safe way!)

E What should I do if I break glassware?

F How should I treat minor heat burns in the laboratory?

G What should I do if I spill a chemical on my skin?

H What should I do if I get a chemical in my eye?

I What should I do if there is an accidental fire in the laboratory?

J What should I do if my clothes catch on fire in the laboratory?

Name _____

Now that you have completed your safety saga, consider the labels below. They are some of the symbols used to communicate hazards with certain chemicals. The labels are part of a system recently introduced called the GHS, or the Globally Harmonized System (see example below). The idea is that they can communicate safety hazards to anyone, anytime, anywhere, even if someone can't read English. Try to determine what these labels mean. Your teacher will confirm your guesses later.

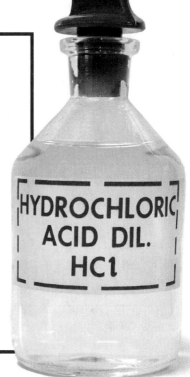

Hydrochloric Acid 33%

DANGER

Causes severe skin burns and eye damage. May cause respiratory irritation.

Do not breathe mist, vapors, spray. Wash exposed skin thoroughly after handling. Use only outdoors or in a well-ventilated area. Wear protective gloves, eye protection, protective clothing. IF SWALLOWED: Rinse mouth. Do NOT induce vomiting.

See SDS for further information.

Fill Weight: 3.91 lbs   Lot Number: LD14261
Gross Weight: 4 lbs   Fill Date: 10/02/2020
Expiration Date: 10/02/2027

ChemLabs • 7705 Lyndon Dr • Detroit, MI 48238 USA • www.chemlabs.com • 800-563-8940

1. _____   4. _____

2. _____   5. _____

3. _____   6. _____

Now look at the Safety Data Sheet (SDS) document that your teacher has given you. Laboratories keep these in an accessible notebook so that people can easily consult them. They are also available in digital form. Answer the following questions about your SDS.

7. Give the product name for the chemical whose SDS you have.

_____

8. List any synonyms for this substance (a maximum of three).

_____

9. What is the percentage composition of this substance?

_____

10. What are the potential effect(s) that this chemical will have for each of the following types of exposure?

eye contact

_____

skin contact

_____

inhalation

_____

ingestion

_____

11. What first aid is recommended for each kind of exposure?

eye contact

_____

_____

skin contact

_____

_____

inhalation

_____

_____

ingestion

_____

_____

12. What personal protection is recommended?

_____

13. Describe each of the following physical characteristics for the chemical. Write n/a if no information is given.

melting point

_____

boiling point

_____

solubility in water

_____

color

_____

14. Is your chemical stable?

_____

15. Is it designated as being incompatible with any specific substances? If so, with what?

_____

I have read the Laboratory Safety and First-Aid Rules in Appendix A and have located all the safety equipment in the laboratory.

Signature _____ **Date** _____

.Name _____

Date _____

Needle in a Haystack

Separating Mixtures

In 1898 chemist-physicist Marie Curie was up against a tremendous challenge. She was trying to isolate two unknown radioactive elements in an ore called *uraninite*, which is a mixture of about thirty different substances. The more abundant of the two unknown elements represents just 0.000 000 1% of the uraninite's total mass! The second element represents even less. It was like looking for a needle in a haystack.

After four years, Curie had isolated 0.1 g of radium from a 1000 kg sample of uraninite. In this lab activity, you will do something similar. Remembering that a mixture is a physical combination of substances, you will use the physical properties of three substances to isolate them from the mixture. Let's tackle that haystack!

How can I separate a mixture even when the components are similar?

QUESTIONS

» How can I separate a mixture?

» How can I analyze the composition of a mixture?

» How can I assess my ability to separate the components of a mixture?

EQUIPMENT

- laboratory balance
- hot plate
- Erlenmeyer flask, 250 mL
- spatula
- weighing dish
- beaker, 150 mL
- bar magnet
- filtering funnel
- clay triangle
- ring stand and ring
- graduated cylinder, 10 mL
- wire gauze
- beaker, 250 mL
- watch glasses, 150 mm (2)
- filter paper
- plastic sandwich bag
- sand, salt, iron mixture, 2–3 g
- goggles

Procedure

A Measure the masses of the flask, filter paper, and plastic bag. Record your results in Table 1. Refer to Appendix C on laboratory techniques for help in measuring mass.

B Using the laboratory balance, spatula, and weighing dish, measure out between 2–3 g of the sand, salt, and iron mixture. Record the mass in Table 1. Transfer the mixture to the 150 mL beaker.

1. Is it possible to separate this mixture by hand or by using a sieve or strainer? Explain.

_____

_____

_____

2. Identify physical properties of the three components that are significantly different and might be useful for separating the mixture.

_____

_____

_____

SEPARATING THE IRON

C Insert the bar magnet into the plastic bag and then stir the mixture in the beaker with the magnet until all the iron filings are removed from the mixture.

D Carefully invert the bag, capturing the iron filings. Remove the magnet. Measure the mass of the bag and iron and record your data in Table 1.

3. What is the purpose of the plastic bag in Step C?

_____

_____

SEPARATING THE SAND

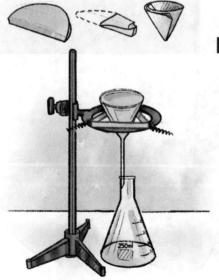

E Fold a piece of filter paper as shown in Appendix C. Shape the filter paper into a cone and insert it into the funnel. Moisten the paper with water and press it against the funnel wall.

F Set the funnel in the clay triangle as it rests on the ring stand's ring. Lower the ring until the tip of the funnel stem touches the inside rim of the flask as shown in the image at left. (When the funnel stem touches another surface, it drains better.)

G Pour the remaining mixture from the beaker into the filter paper. You may need to tap the beaker with a pen or pencil to dislodge any particles that adhere to the sides or bottom.

H Using the graduated cylinder, slowly pour four portions of hot tap water (approximately 5 mL each) over the mixture. The liquid—called the *filtrate*—will collect in the flask. Allow each 5 mL portion to run through the mixture before adding the next. Pour the final 5 mL of water around the upper edge of the filter paper.

4. Is the water in the flask still plain water? Explain.

_____

_____

_____

5. Why do you think that you used hot water for this step? Would you have expected different results had you used cold water instead? Explain.

_____

_____

_____

6. Identify physical properties of salt and water that are significantly different and that might be useful for separating this new mixture. What about the water and sand mixture?

_____

_____

_____

_____

SEPARATING THE SALT

I Place the flask containing the salt solution on the hot plate, turn the hot plate on medium-high, and bring the liquid to a gentle boil. Allow the salt water to simmer until most of the water has been boiled off and crystals begin to appear in the dish. ***Do not heat so strongly that splattering occurs.***

J Turn the hot plate to low and continue evaporating the water. When no water is visible, turn off the hot plate and allow the residual heat to evaporate the remaining water. ***Do not heat dry glassware.***

K While you are waiting for the salt solution to evaporate, carefully spread the filter paper containing the sand onto a watch glass. Set the watch glass at the base of the burner. By the time your salt solution has evaporated, the sand and filter paper should also be dry. (If they are not dry by the time the solution has evaporated, leave them overnight and do Step M the next day.)

L Once the flask is cool, measure the mass of the flask and salt and record your data in Table 1.

M When the sand and filter paper are dry, measure the mass and record your data in Table 1.

7. Why did you have to take such care in evaporating the water from the saltwater mixture? Why not just heat the water vigorously until it all boiled away?

_____

_____

_____

Analysis

N Calculate the masses of the iron, salt, and sand recovered. Record your answer in Table 2.

O Calculate the total mass recovered and record your answer in Table 2.

When dealing with combinations of materials, it is common to calculate the percent composition. The formula below can be used to calculate the percentage of each of the three components.

$$\% \text{ composition} = \left(\frac{\text{component mass}}{\text{total mass}}\right)100\%$$

8. Use the space below to calculate the percent composition of the iron. Record your answer in Table 2. Repeat for salt and sand.

9. Obtain the original percent composition from your teacher. How do your percent composition calculations compare? Explain any discrepancies.

_____

_____

_____

_____

10. On the basis of your experimental percent compositions and the percent composition of the original mixture, how well do you think you did at separating the mixture? Explain.

_____

_____

Scientists will many times need to know how efficiently they have accomplished a task. When working in chemistry, we are often interested in how much of the original sample we ended up with. We can use percent recovered to check our efficiency.

$$\% \text{ recovered} = \left(\frac{m_{\text{recovered}}}{m_{\text{initial}}}\right)100\%$$

11. Use the space below to calculate the percent recovered and record your data in Table 2.

12. Did you recover all of the original sample? If not, explain possible reasons for this discrepancy. How well do you think you did at recovering the sample?

_____

_____

13. Why was it necessary to find the mass of the flask, filter paper, and plastic bag at the beginning of the experiment?

_____

_____

TABLE 1: *Data*

Object	Mass (g)
flask	
filter paper	
plastic bag	
mixture, initial	
plastic bag and iron	
flask and salt	
filter paper and sand	

TABLE 2: *Results*

Object	Mass (g)	Percent Recovered	Percent Composition
iron, recovered			
salt, recovered			
sand, recovered			
mixture, recovered			

Name _____

Date _____

EQUIPMENT

- laboratory burner and lighter
- magnifying glass
- bar magnet
- deflagration spoon
- spatula
- graduated cylinder, 10 mL
- test tubes (3)
- test tube rack
- weighing paper (8 pcs.)
- iron (Fe) filings
- sulfur (S) powder or granules
- iron(II) sulfide (FeS)
- iron and sulfur mixture
- hydrochloric acid (HCl), 6 M, 7.5 mL
- goggles
- laboratory apron
- nitrile gloves

Zebroids, Wolphins, and Ligers, Oh My!

Classifying Matter

Did you know that zebras and horses can produce offspring together? So can whales and dolphins, and tigers and lions. These animal hybrids definitely look different from either of their parents! People have learned how to breed animals and plants such as horses and wheat to increase their productivity and use for mankind. Chemists do something similar when they form new substances for specific purposes.

Does physically or chemically combining elements change their properties?

Today we'll explore how two chemicals change when they come together to form a completely new substance with its own custom set of physical and chemical properties. In this lab activity, you will observe the properties of iron filings, sulfur powder, a mixture of iron filings and sulfur powder, and the compound iron(II) sulfide. You will see under what conditions the physical and chemical properties change.

QUESTION

» What properties are helpful in classifying mixtures?

Procedure

A Using the spatula, obtain pea-sized samples of iron, sulfur, the iron-sulfur mixture, and iron(II) sulfide (FeS), and place them on separate pieces of weighing paper.

B Describe the physical appearance of each sample, noting any differences between them. Use a magnifying glass to aid your inspection. Record your observations in Table 1.

You've seen how matter can be classified either as a pure substance or as a mixture. Pure substances consist of only a single substance: an element or a compound. Elements consist of only one type of atom, while compounds are chemical combinations of two or more elements in fixed ratios. Mixtures are physical combinations of two or more substances in a changeable ratio.

The classification of matter

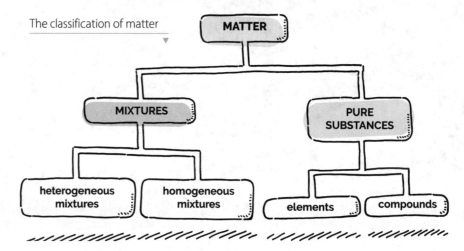

1. From your observation of its physical appearance, determine whether the iron-sulfur mixture is homogeneous or heterogeneous. How can you tell?

_____

_____

_____

2. Would you make the same observation for the compound iron(II) sulfide? Why or why not?

_____

_____

_____

MAGNETISM

C Observe the magnetism of the substances by passing a magnet under each sample. *Keep the weighing paper between the samples and the magnet* so that magnetic substances will not stick to the magnet. Record your observations in Table 1.

3. What happened to the magnetic properties of iron and sulfur when they were combined in a

mixture? What happened when they were chemically combined in iron(II) sulfide?

_____

_____

_____

_____

COMBUSTIBILITY

D Place approximately half of your iron sample on a deflagration spoon and insert it into the hottest part of a laboratory burner flame for about thirty seconds **under a fume hood**. Look for evidence that the iron burned. Record your observations in Table 1. If it burns, allow it to burn completely. Repeat for the other three substances.

4. After the chemicals were burned there was less of them. Was that matter destroyed? Explain.

_____

_____

_____

_____

E If any substance remains after the combustion test, place it on a clean piece of weighing paper and test it with a magnet. Record your observations in Table 1.

REACTIVITY

F Working under the fume hood, pour 7.5 mL of 6 M HCl into your graduated cylinder. Then divide it into nearly equal parts among the three test tubes.

G Drop the remainder of your iron sample into one test tube and observe whether a chemical change occurs (e.g., a color change occurs, a new substance forms, or bubbles form). Repeat for the sulfur and the iron-sulfur mixture. **Do not test the iron(II) sulfide in the acid**. Record your observations in Table 1.

5. What evidence was there to indicate that the iron was reacting with the hydrochloric acid?

_____

_____

_____

_____

H Pour the remaining acid solutions (HCl) into the designated acid waste container located in the fume hood.

Analysis

6. How will you distinguish between a mixture and a compound?

_____

_____

_____

7. How can an iron-sulfur mixture be separated into its elements? Can this method extract elements from iron(II) sulfide?

_____

_____

_____

8. Iron melts at 1538 °C and sulfur melts at 115 °C. Does this information help you determine the melting point of iron(II) sulfide? Explain.

_____

_____

_____

TABLE 1

	Elements		Mixture	Compound
	Iron Filings (Fe)	**Sulfur Powder (S)**	**Iron and Sulfur Mixture**	**Iron(II) Sulfide (FeS)**
What does each sample look like?				
Did the sample exhibit magnetic behavior?				
Did the sample burn?				
If a residue remained, was it magnetic?				
Did the sample react with HCl?				

3A LAB

Metric Unicorns

Exploring the Metric System

Have you ever heard of mutchkins, yojanas, grzywnas, and virgates? They aren't fantastical creatures like ogres, fairies, and unicorns from some enchanted land. They're actually units of measurement! These strange-sounding units of measurement might help us appreciate the standard that the SI system gives us for measuring anything, whether length, luminosity, or electric current. By using a common system, scientists all over the world can exchange information easily and without confusion.

More than likely, you've been measuring things since elementary school, but have you ever really thought about what lies behind measurement? Let's explore the subject by getting out of our comfort zone. We'll do this by inventing a brand-new unit of measure and seeing what we discover.

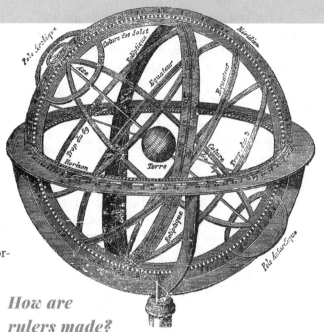

How are rulers made?

Procedure

All measurement units are based on a reference known as a *standard*. Some standards are physical objects, while others are phenomena. To keep things easy, we'll use a physical object—your textbook—as a standard of length.

QUESTIONS

» What goes into creating a new unit of measurement?

» How are metric prefixes helpful?

» How do I determine conversion factors?

» How do I use unit conversion factors?

WORKING WITH THE UNIT

A Create a ruler with a length of one book by cutting a piece of paper tape equal to the length of your textbook's spine.

1. What is the relationship of your paper ruler to the standard?

_____

_____

2. Identify two objects in the room that could be measured with your new ruler.

_____

_____

3. What is a significant limitation of your ruler?

_____

EQUIPMENT

• paper tape
• textbook
• scissors
• metric ruler
• meter stick

To make a measuring tool like a ruler more useful, it must be divided into fractions of a unit. This process is called *graduation*. The more graduations a ruler has, the more *precise* it becomes.

B Fold your ruler in half to find the middle. Unfold the ruler, draw a pencil line down the fold, and label it *5*. Label the left edge of the ruler *0* and the right edge *10*.

C Add four equally spaced lines to the left of the fold labeled *1*, *2*, *3*, and *4*. Then add four equally spaced lines to the right of the fold labeled *6*, *7*, *8*, and *9*. Use only your eyes to space the lines. Do the best that you can!

D Finally, divide the first division (between *0* and *1*) into ten small divisions by drawing nine equally spaced tick marks along the edge of the paper.

4. Using the standard metric prefixes, what would you call the large divisions? the small ones?

_____

_____

5. What was the smallest marking of the ruler originally? After adding tick marks, what was the smallest marking on the ruler between 0 and 0.1?

_____

_____

6. With what precision should you measure using the ruler as originally marked? After graduation, with what precision could you measure between 0 and 0.1?

_____

_____

_____

_____

Recall that when making measurements, you read all of certain digits and then estimate the next whole decimal place. For example, if you are using a ruler marked to 0.01 cm, then you can make measurements to the thousandths place.

E Using your improved ruler, measure the width of your hand and record the value in Table 1. Come up with a symbol for your base unit of books and enter it in the column header of Table 1. Also enter the two additional prefixed units that your ruler allows for.

F Express your measurement to the same precision but using the two prefix-scaled units. Record your values in Table 1.

7. What is a serious limitation to your improved ruler? Does a commercially produced metric ruler have this limitation? Explain.

_____

_____

_____

_____

We've measured things smaller than a book with your new unit. Now let's measure things much bigger than a book.

G Create a tape measure with a length of ten books by cutting a piece of paper tape ten times the length of your textbook's spine. Mark and number 1-book divisions on the tape.

8. Using a standard metric prefix, what is the name of this new unit of length? Enter the new prefixed unit that your tape measure allows for.

_____

H Using the tape measure, measure the length of your classroom. Record the value in Table 1.

I Express your measurement to the same precision but in the new unit and record the value in Table 1.

CONVERTING UNITS

Sometimes it's necessary to change between two different units. But in order to perform this task, you need to know the relationship between the two units. A *conversion factor* expresses this relationship, either as a fraction or as an equation. For example, 1 m = 3.28 ft. Let's create a conversion factor to convert between centimeters and books.

J Using the metric ruler, measure your 1-book ruler to the nearest 0.1 cm.

9. Create a conversion factor that relates books to centimeters.

   _____

10. Using your conversion factor from Question 9, convert the measurement of your hand in books to centimeters. Use the space below to show your work. Record this value in Table 1.

K Using the meter stick, measure your dekabook tape.

11. Create a conversion factor that relates dekabooks to meters. Write your conversion factor in either fractional or equation form.

   _____

12. Using your conversion factor from Question 11, convert the measurement of your classroom in dekabooks to meters. Use the space below to show your work. Record this value in Table 1.

Analysis

13. Using what you've learned from your textbook, state why your textbook is a good standard for measurement.

   _____

   _____

   _____

   _____

14. Again, using what you've learned from your textbook, state why your textbook is *not* a good standard for measurement.

_____

_____

_____

_____

15. Why do we generally avoid creating customized measuring units such as the one that you created in this lab activity?

_____

_____

_____

_____

16. Discuss how standardized measuring systems are an example of good dominion that is pleasing to God.

_____

_____

_____

_____

_____

_____

TABLE 1

Object	Width	Width	Width	Width	Width (cm)	Width (m)
hand						
room						

3B LAB

Name _____

Date _____

You Are My Density

Inquiring into Measurement

Intensive properties, such as density, are ones that remain constant regardless of the amount of material in a sample. Therefore, density is useful for identifying substances. Recall that density is defined as the mass per unit of volume ($\rho = m/V$). In the metric system, density has the units g/mL or g/cm³ for liquids and solids and g/L for gases.

How do different methods affect the accuracy of experimental methods?

In this inquiry lab activity, you will develop procedures to determine the density of two objects. Both objects are mixtures of elements. From your density data, you will then estimate the percent composition of each object.

QUESTIONS

» How do I design a lab activity?

» How can I use density to help identify the composition of an object?

» How accurately can I measure?

EQUIPMENT

- penny
- coil of solder
- goggles

Procedure

PLANNING/WRITING SCIENTIFIC QUESTIONS

A Obtain a penny and a coil of solder from your teacher.

B Brainstorm with your lab group about how you can determine the density of each object.

C Brainstorm with your lab group about how you can use your density data to determine the elements that make up each object.

D Write specific questions related to calculating the density of each object that you could answer by collecting data.

DESIGNING SCIENTIFIC INVESTIGATIONS

E Write procedures to collect data that will allow you to answer the questions that you wrote in Step D above.

F Have your teacher approve your procedures.

CONDUCTING SCIENTIFIC INVESTIGATIONS

G Following the procedures that you have written, collect the data to answer the questions that you wrote.

H From Table 1, select some possible metals that your objects may contain. Other physical properties can help you make a determination.

I Assuming that the solder is made of copper and one other metal in a 41/59 ratio, use your density data to determine the other metal.

J Assuming that a penny is made of only copper and zinc, use your density data to determine the proportions of copper and zinc.

K Look up the actual proportions of zinc and copper in pennies. Make a claim about the accuracy of your process. Support your claim with evidence from your prediction and test.

TABLE 1

Metal	Density (g/cm³)
aluminum	2.75
copper	8.96
gold	19.30
iron	7.87
lead	11.34
magnesium	1.74
nickel	8.90
silver	10.49
tin	7.26
zinc	7.14

4 LAB

Name _____

Date _____

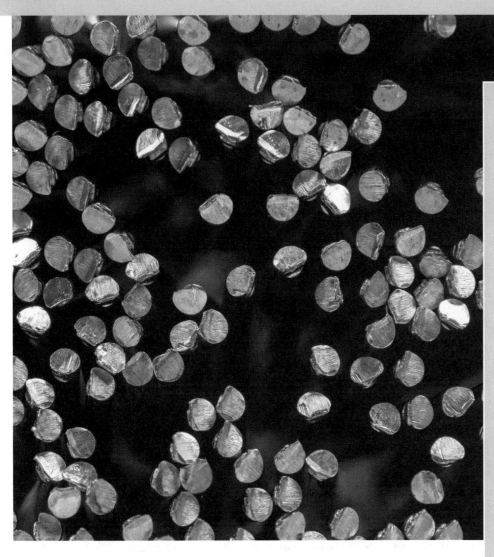

All that Glitters Is Not Copper-63

Investigating Mixtures of Isotopes

Pennies are made of copper, right? Well, sort of. Pennies minted before 1982 were made of 95% copper. But starting in that year, because of the rising cost of copper, the US Mint started making pennies from 97.5% zinc with a thin copper coating. That means that not all pennies in circulation today have the same composition, even though they are all pennies.

Copper atoms are not all alike either. They exist as one of two different but common and stable isotopes—copper-63 and copper-65. On the periodic table, the atomic mass of copper is not listed as either 63 or 65, but 63.55. Why is this? Copper, like most naturally occurring elements, is a mixtures of isotopes. The atomic masses listed on the periodic table are *weighted averages* of the various isotopes of each element.

Why are the masses on the periodic table not whole numbers?

QUESTIONS

» How do I determine the weighted average mass of a mixture of isotopes?

» How do I determine the percent composition of a mixture?

We calculate average atomic mass by dividing the total mass of all the atoms by the total number of atoms.

$$\text{average atomic mass} = \frac{m_{total}}{n_{total}}$$

To determine the total mass, we sum the masses of each isotope (kind of atom). The formula for this calculation is shown below.

$$\text{total mass} = \sum m_{isotope} \, n_{atoms}$$

The Greek letter Σ indicates "to take the sum of." If we were taking the sum of the masses of only two isotopes, the total mass would be calculated as shown below.

$$m_{total} = \sum m_{isotope} \, n_{atoms} = \overbrace{m_{isotope\,1} \, n_{atoms\,of\,isotope\,1}}^{\text{Isotope 1}} + \overbrace{m_{isotope\,2} \, n_{atoms\,of\,isotope\,2}}^{\text{Isotope 2}}$$

So the formula for calculating the average atomic mass is

$$\text{average atomic mass} = \frac{\sum m_{isotope} \, n_{atoms}}{\sum n_{atoms}}.$$

In this investigation, you will use a mixture of two varieties of chocolate-covered candies to represent two different isotopes in 1 mol of the "element" emenemium.

Procedure

A   Obtain a mixture of fifty candies from your teacher.

B   Find the mass of five large candies and five small candies. Remember that we always report one estimated digit in our measurements. Record these masses in Table 1.

C   Calculate the average mass for each type of candy. Record these values in Table 1. Don't forget significant figures!

1. A student from a different class mentioned that when they divided the mass of their five large candies (10.67 g) by five to calculate the average, they got 2.134. The lab partners couldn't agree whether that should be reported as 2.134 g or 2.13 g. How do you reply?

_____

_____

_____

_____

_____

D   Count the total number of both large and small candies in your mixture and record your data in Table 1.

Analysis

Now you will calculate the weighted average of the masses of candies in the mixture as instructed below. Refer to Example 4-3 on page 89 of your textbook. Be sure to follow the rules for significant figures.

E Do not measure the mass of your mixture. Calculate the total mass of your sample of candies and record your data in Table 2.

F Measure the total mass of your mixture of candies and record your data in Table 2.

G Calculate the percent error between your calculated total mass and the actual total mass of your mixture and record your calculation in Table 2.

H Calculate the weighted average mass of a candy piece from your calculated total mass of your sample and record your data in Table 2.

2. How does this calculation relate to average atomic masses for elements?

_____

_____

◻ Using the average mass of each candy and the average candy mass for the entire mixture, calculate the percentage of each "isotope" in the candy mixture.

Record your data in Table 1.

J Now verify the percent calculations from Step I using the numbers of candies ("isotopes") that are used. Record your data in Table 1.

3. Account for any differences between the answers for Steps I and J.

_____

_____

4. Now explain why the atomic mass on the periodic table for copper is not a whole number. Which isotope is more common in natural copper?

_____

_____

Copper has twenty-seven other isotopes, all of which are radioactive, or *radioisotopes*. You'll learn more about radioisotopes in Chapter 22. These isotopes are unstable, short-lived, and relatively rare.

5. How would radioisotopes of copper affect the atomic mass of copper on the periodic table?

_____

_____

6. The radioisotopes of copper are very useful in medicine for making images of the body and for treating cancers. Where do you think scientists get these radioisotopes?

_____

_____

7. How can the chemistry of copper be used to fulfill God's commands to love and serve others?

_____

_____

_____

_____

TABLE 1

Object	Mass of Five (g)	Average Mass (g/candy)	Number in Mixture	%_{composition} from Mass	%_{composition} from Number of Candies
Large Candies					
Small Candies					

TABLE 2

Object	Total Mass (calculated) (g)	Total Mass (measured) (g)	% Error	Average Atomic Mass (g)
Mixture				

5A LAB

Bulls-Eye!

Modeling an Atomic Orbital

We commonly see an atom depicted as a nucleus surrounded by a number of electrons traveling in circular orbits. But as physicists learned more about atoms, they quickly deduced that electrons do not travel in neatly defined orbits. Instead, they are found in indistinct regions called *orbitals*. What does an orbital look like? And what is the difference between an orbital in one level and another found in a higher energy level?

Procedure

ATOMS WITH LOW-ENERGY ORBITALS FILLED

Select one lab partner to be the "dropper" and the other to be the "catcher."

A Place a target sheet flat on a hard floor.

B The dropper should hold the marble over the target sheet at waist level, aim at the X, and release the marble.

C The catcher should catch the marble after it bounces the first time, before it can strike the paper a second time.

D Repeat Steps B and C ninety-nine additional times. Use a scratch piece of paper to keep a tally of how many times the marble is dropped.

E Using a compass, draw a circle on the target sheet such that ninety of the hits are inside the circle, leaving ten of the hits outside the circle.

1. If the X on the paper represents the nucleus of an atom, what do you think the impression left by each marble drop represents?

_____

_____

QUESTIONS

» How can I model electron orbitals?

» How is the energy of an electron related to the size of its orbital?

Why can't we know exactly where electrons are located?

EQUIPMENT

- carbonless paper targets (2)
- marble or ball bearing
- drawing compass
- meter stick

F Repeat Steps A through E using the second target. This time, though, drop the marble from eye level rather than waist level.

2. What does each marble represent in this second set of drops?

_____

_____

Analysis

G Measure the radius of each circle and record your measurements in Table 1.

3. How do the radii of the two targets compare?

_____

_____

4. What does the size of the circle represent in this particular atomic model?

_____

_____

5. Does the variation in target size make sense? Explain.

_____

_____

6. Why didn't all the dropped marbles land in the same spot?

_____

_____

7. Compare the distribution of "electrons" between the two targets. How does the distribution change with the height of the dropped marbles? How does this model the arrangement of electrons in an actual atom?

_____

_____

_____

_____

H Create a scatterplot of the atomic radius versus the drop height. Include a curve of best fit that includes the origin as a data point.

8. When you include (0, 0) as a point on your graph, is the relationship linear? Explain.

_____

_____

9. Your target model is, of course, a two-dimensional representation of a three-dimensional structure. What would the circle drawn on each target look like in a three-dimensional model?

_____

10. Describe the shapes of the orbitals depicted in your textbook.

_____

_____

11. On the basis of your descriptions from Questions 9 and 10, do you think that the circular orbital depicted in this lab activity is a good model for all the electrons in an atom?

_____

_____

_____

_____

_____

Going Further

12. In what way(s) does using a dropped marble aimed at a target do a good job of modeling the locations of electrons? In what way(s) does it fall short?

_____

_____

_____

_____

_____

_____

_____

TABLE 1

Target	Drop Height (m)	Atomic Radius (cm)
1	1.0	
2	2.0	

Name _____

Date _____

Seeing Light in a New Way

Exploring Spectroscopy

News flash! Our solar system is not the only one out there. As of 2020, scientists have confirmed the existence of more than 4100 other planets that are orbiting stars other than our sun. How did scientists know that they were exoplanets and not something else, like a distant galaxy or star?

Light from stars gives us information. Some of this light is visible, but some of it is in forms that we can't see, such as gamma rays, x-rays, microwaves, and radio waves. Visible light can tell us the elements that make up stars and the speed that stars are moving relative to Earth. Scientists usually find an exoplanet when it passes in front of a star, dimming the light for a short period of time. To get information from a star, astronomers use a tool called a *spectroscope*. Although any form of electromagnetic radiation could theoretically be used in spectroscopy, scientists often work with visible light because it is easiest to observe.

How can light be used to identify elements?

Visible light, like other kinds of radiation in the electromagnetic spectrum, can be either emitted or absorbed by atoms when their electrons move to a lower energy level or jump to a higher energy level. This means that scientists can distinguish two kinds of visible light spectra—emission spectra and absorption spectra. Emission spectra show the wavelengths of light that something puts out by showing lines of light on a black background. See page 95 of your textbook for a picture of an emission spectra. Absorption spectra show the wavelengths of light that something absorbs by showing lines of black on the background of a continuous spectrum. Both absorption and emission spectra are line spectra.

In this lab activity, you'll learn just how informative light can be. You'll observe the emission spectra of several salts using a simple diffraction grating spectroscope. After sketching these spectra, you'll use your sketches to reveal the secret identity of an unknown salt.

EQUIPMENT

- diffraction grating spectroscope
- laboratory burner and lighter
- beaker, 100 mL
- incandescent light source
- colored pencils
- chloride salts
- nitrate salts
- presoaked wooden splints
- LED light source
- fluorescent light source
- goggles
- laboratory apron

QUESTIONS

» How do elements produce visible light?

» Why do different elements produce different colors of light?

» How can we use a diffraction grating to study light?

» What is the relationship between the color of light and the electrons in an atom?

Procedure

Incandescent light bulbs produce light when electricity runs through a fine tungsten wire called a *filament*. This filament begins to glow, producing visible light as electrons are excited by an increase in temperature and jump to higher energy levels. As electrons return to lower energy levels, they release a variety of visible light wavelengths.

A Observe the spectrum of an incandescent light by looking at it through your spectroscope. Note the calibration marks (400–800 nm) in the spectrum below. Use colored pencils to sketch the spectrum or label the colors that you observe. Add the let-

ters ROYGBIV (representing red, orange, yellow, green, blue, indigo, and violet) at the appropriate locations.

1. What kind of spectrum does an incandescent light bulb emit? What color is this kind of light?

_____

_____

_____

_____

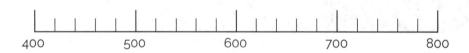

B Obtain three pairs of samples of certain nitrate and chloride salts that your teacher has chosen. The salt samples should be in pairs according to their metal ions (e.g., sodium nitrate and sodium chloride).

C Fill the beaker with water and keep it close by.

D Light your laboratory burner. Adjust the burner until it produces a blue or colorless flame.

E The wooden splints that you will be using have been soaked in water overnight. Dip a presoaked splint into either of the first pair of salt samples and then insert the salt-encrusted tip into the hottest part of the burner's flame (see below). Record the flame color that is produced by the salt in Table 1. If the splint catches fire, simply douse it in the beaker of water that you prepared in Step C.

F Repeat Step E for the other salt in the pair.

G Repeat Steps E and F for the remaining salt pairs.

2. Which element in these compounds do you think is responsible for the color change? How can you tell?

_____

_____

_____

_____

3. What do you think is happening to the electrons in these atoms that causes them to emit visible light? Where do the colors come from?

_____

_____

_____

_____

_____

_____

ELEMENTS AND SPECTRA

H Now that you have found which element in these compounds is responsible for the color change in the flame test, obtain other chloride salts that your teacher has provided.

I Dip a presoaked splint and have your lab partner look through the spectroscope at the flame. Put the tip of the splint in the flame long enough for the salt to burn as you did before, noting its color before the wooden splint begins to burn. Record your observation in Table 1.

J Have your lab partner observe the spectrum that forms. It will probably be different than when looking at an incandescent light bulb! Use the spectrum graphs on pages 42–43 to sketch the emission spectra of your flame tests. Either label or color the bright lines with colored pencils to identify them. Switch roles with your lab partner so that each of you observes the burning splints while using the spectroscope. If you need to see a flame test again, use a fresh presoaked splint and a fresh sample of salt.

K Repeat Steps I and J for the remaining salts, using a new splint for each test.

4. How does a spectroscope help you identify elements in a flame test?

_____

_____

_____

5. What did you notice when you compared the colors of the flame and the line spectra?

_____

_____

_____

MYSTERY SALT

L Now to solve a mystery! Your teacher will give you two unknown salts. Do a flame test of each salt, and sketch its emission spectra in the appropriate spectral graphs on page 43.

6. What was the identity of the chloride salt Unknown 1?

_____

7. What was the identity of the chloride salt Unknown 2?

_____

Analysis

8. Since each element produces a characteristic spectrum, what can you conclude about the location of the electrons?

_____

9. Suppose that you had used the same wooden splint to burn all the salts in succession. What difficulty could this have introduced?

_____

_____

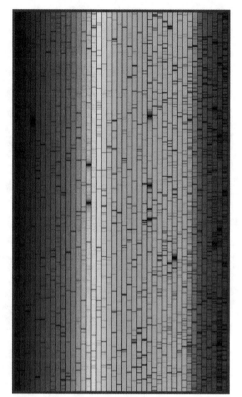

Look at the absorption spectrum from a star shown at left. The black lines display wavelengths of light that are absorbed by the gases in the star.

10. Why is this information useful?

_____

_____

11. If emission lines are created in a spectrum when an electron falls from an excited state to a less energetic state, how would you explain absorption lines?

_____

_____

_____

Going Further

ARTIFICIAL LIGHTS AND SPECTRA

In this lab activity, you have been looking at emission spectra of different elements. These bright lines are emitted when atoms receive energy that causes one or more of the atom's valence electrons to jump from their original positions to higher energy orbitals and almost immediately fall back to lower orbitals, emitting visible light. The wavelengths (colors) of the light depend on the energy differences between the atom's various orbitals. As a result, atoms of each element generate characteristic lines of colors. You also looked at the emission spectra of an incandescent bulb, which produced a continuous spectrum rather than lines.

LED (light-emitting diode) bulbs make light by the movement of electrons through *semiconductors*, materials that contain elements such as silicon and antimony. They don't have filaments like incandescent bulbs do. They produce light just like the elements in your flame test: the electrons are excited to higher energy levels and then return to lower ones.

M Observe the emission spectrum of an LED bulb by looking at it with your spectroscope. Sketch the spectrum in the appropriate spectral graph on page 43.

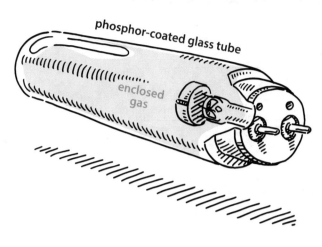

phosphor-coated glass tube

enclosed gas

Fluorescent bulbs make light in a different way. They contain a gas that produces ultraviolet light when electricity excites electrons. The reason that the electrons don't produce visible light is because the jump between energy levels is larger and releases ultraviolet light, which humans can't see. The inside of the bulb is coated with *phosphors*. Phosphors are chemicals that glow when they are exposed to ultraviolet light, emitting visible light as their electrons move between energy levels. So fluorescent bulbs convert electricity to visible light in a multistep process.

N Observe the emission spectrum of a fluorescent bulb by looking at it with your spectroscope. Sketch the spectrum in the appropriate spectral graph on page 43.

12. You may have noticed that the spectra of some artificial lights were different than those of the incandescent light. Compare and contrast both the color of the light and the spectra.

_____

_____

_____

_____

13. What type of lamp would produce light in which different-colored objects look the most natural? Why?

_____

_____

_____

_____

14. Can you think of any settings in which very good lighting is essential for work and productivity?

_____

_____

_____

_____

Salt name: _____

Color of the flame: _____

400   500   600   700   800

Salt name: _____

Color of the flame: _____

400   500   600   700   800

Salt name: _____

Color of the flame: _____

400   500   600   700   800

Salt name: _____

Color of the flame: _____

400   500   600   700   800

Salt name: _____

Color of the flame: _____

400   500   600   700   800

Salt name: _____

Color of the flame: _____

400   500   600   700   800

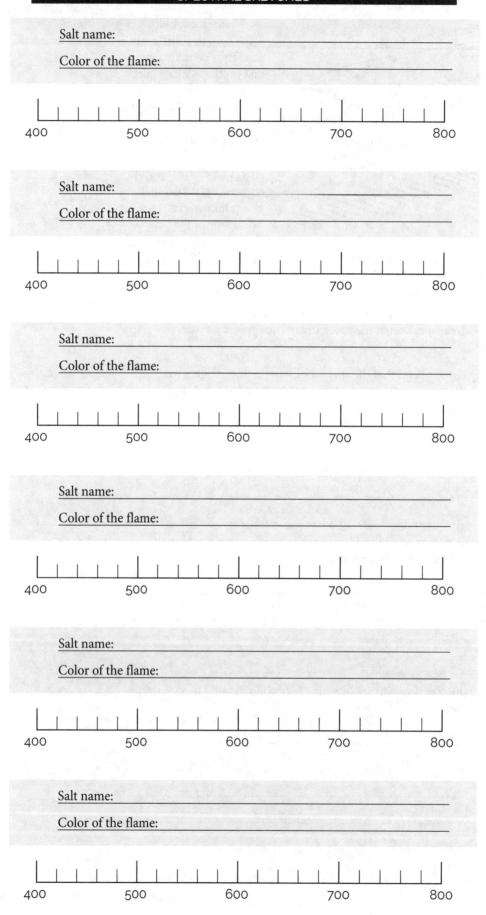

Salt name: _____

Color of the flame: _____

| | | | | | | | | | | | | | | | | | | | |
400   500   600   700   800

Salt name: _____

Color of the flame: _____

400   500   600   700   800

Unknown 1

Color of the flame: _____

400   500   600   700   800

Unknown 2

Color of the flame: _____

400   500   600   700   800

LED bulb

_____

400   500   600   700   800

Fluorescent bulb

_____

400   500   600   700   800

TABLE 1

Chloride Salt	Color Observed	Nitrate Salt	Color Observed

Name _____

Date _____

EQUIPMENT

- small plastic cups (7) with samples
- goggles
- laboratory apron
- nitrile gloves

Exposed to the Elements

Inquiring into Properties of Elements

Throughout history, people have made bridges out of different materials. We have made them from wood, stone, steel, and concrete. Why have we used these materials for building bridges? Each one has properties that make it good for constructing a bridge. Engineers try to match the properties of materials with the physical requirements of the object that is being built.

How do we classify elements?

There are currently 118 known elements. Each element has different physical and chemical properties. As scientists discovered elements, they recognized that they would need a way to organize them. Some scientists made lists and others made tables. As the periodic table of the elements was developed, scientists were surprised to discover that individual elements had properties that were similar to other elements located nearby on the table.

In this lab activity, you will observe the properties of various elements.

Procedure

RESEARCH

1. What are the general characteristics of metals, nonmetals, and metalloids? Use your textbook or other resources as needed.

_____

_____

_____

_____

_____

_____

QUESTIONS

» How do metals, nonmetals, and metalloids compare?

» How can I use the characteristics of metals, nonmetals, or metalloids to classify them?

PLANNING/WRITING SCIENTIFIC QUESTIONS

A Brainstorm with your lab group about how you could test the seven samples provided by your teacher to enable you to classify each element as either a metal, nonmetal, or metalloid.

B Write specific questions related to the samples and the characteristics of metals, nonmetals, and metalloids that you could answer by collecting data.

DESIGNING SCIENTIFIC INVESTIGATIONS

C Write procedures to collect data that will enable you to answer the questions that you wrote in Step B above.

D Have your teacher approve your procedures.

CONDUCTING SCIENTIFIC INVESTIGATIONS

E Following the procedures that you have written, collect data to answer the questions that you wrote.

DEVELOPING MODELS

F Organize your data in a table. Include in the table your classification of each element as a metal, nonmetal, or metalloid.

G Obtain the identification of the elements from your teacher. Consult a periodic table to see whether your classification matches the organization of the periodic table.

SCIENTIFIC ARGUMENTATION

H Make a claim about the accuracy of your classification of the elements that you tested. Support your claim with evidence from your prediction and test.

An Elemental Merry-Go-Round

Exploring Periodic Trends

Periodic tables are not "one size fits all." They can use spirals, steps, circles, and even amoeba shapes to communicate information about how the properties of elements change with their atomic number. The regular repetition of the properties of elements is described by the *periodic law*.

Regardless of the shape of a periodic table, elements with similar properties are located in similar positions in the table. In the traditional periodic table, the elements with similar properties are in the vertical columns. For example, since lithium, sodium, potassium, rubidium, and cesium have similar reactivity, they are placed in a vertical column. We call vertical columns *groups*, or *families*, and horizontal rows *periods*, or *series*. Properties vary as you move across a period or down a group.

So just how periodic is the periodic table? In this lab activity, you will graph the trends of four different properties: atomic radius, electronegativity, electron affinity, and ionization energy. You will then use these graphs to predict the properties of other elements. You will also explore how atomic radii increase across a period and down a group of the periodic table.

What does the periodic table tell us about chemical and physical properties?

© 2021 BJU Press. Reproduction prohibited.

QUESTIONS

» How do atomic radii and atomic numbers vary along the periodic table?

» How can I predict the atomic radius of an element on the basis of periodic patterns?

» How is the periodic table a type of model?

EQUIPMENT

• computer with spreadsheet software

The main idea of this spiral periodic table is to show the periodic nature of the elements. Makes you think of a merry-go-round!

PERIODICITY ←

ATOMIC RADIUS

Atomic radius is the average distance from the nucleus to the outermost electrons in an atom. Atomic radii range from a billionth to a trillionth of a meter. You can imagine how difficult it would be to measure these values. There are a number of techniques that scientists use to measure the radius of an atom. The atomic radii values in Table 1 are *covalent radii*. The covalent radius is one of the measures that scientists use for atomic radius.

A Using a spreadsheet program and the data from Table 1, create a scatterplot of the atomic radii given. Plot the atomic number on the *x*-axis and the atomic radii on the *y*-axis.

1. What general trends do you notice on the graph of atomic radii?

_____

_____

_____

B Label the major peaks on the graph with the symbol of the appropriate element.

2. Which elements occupy the peaks in your graph of atomic radii?

_____

_____

_____

3. Where are these elements on the periodic table?

_____

_____

4. Are there any areas of your graph that seem to contradict the pattern?

_____

_____

_____

5. Using this graph, predict the radii of magnesium (12), iron (26), and lead (82).

_____

_____

_____

6. Using your graph of atomic radii, indicate the general trend across a period and down a column of the periodic table.

_____

_____

_____

ELECTRONEGATIVITY

Electronegativity is a chemical property indicating the attraction of an atom for electrons that it shares with other atoms when it bonds. The electronegativity values in Table 1 are based on the Pauling scale.

C Create a scatterplot of the electronegativity values. Plot the atomic number on the *x*-axis and the electronegativity on the *y*-axis.

7. What general trends do you notice on the graph of electronegativity? How does it compare with the atomic radius graph?

_____

_____

_____

_____

D Label the major peaks on your electronegativity graph with the symbol of the appropriate element.

8. Which elements occupy the first four peaks of the cycles shown in your graph?

_____

_____

9. Where are these elements on the periodic table?

_____

_____

10. Using this graph, predict the electronegativity values for magnesium (12), iron (26), and selenium (34).

_____

_____

11. Using your graph of electronegativity, indicate the general trend across a period and down a column of the periodic table.

_____

_____

_____

_____

ELECTRON AFFINITY

Electron affinity is a measure of the amount of energy released when an electron is added to a neutral atom to make it a negatively charged anion. The electron affinity values in Table 1 are measured in kJ/mol.

E Create a third scatterplot with atomic number on the x-axis and electron affinity on the y-axis.

12. What general trends do you notice on the graph of electron affinity?

_____

_____

_____

_____

FIRST IONIZATION ENERGY

The first ionization energy of an atom is the minimum amount of energy needed to remove an electron from a neutral atom. The first ionization energy values in Table 1 are given in electronvolts (eV).

F Make a fourth scatterplot showing atomic number on the x-axis and first ionization energy on the y-axis.

13. What general trends do you notice on the graph of first ionization energy? What graph does it look similar to?

_____

_____

_____

_____

_____

14. Do the peaks of this graph match those in the graph that you created in Step C? Explain.

_____

_____

15. In the last three segments, there should be a series of four or five elements that significantly deviate from the pattern. Is there a pattern to the location of these elements on the periodic table?

_____

_____

_____

_____

_____

16. Would it be useful to organize the elements in an alphabetized table? Why or why not?

_____

_____

_____

_____

17. How is the periodic table an example of a model in science? (See pages 1–2 of your textbook.)

_____

_____

_____

_____

_____

Going Further

18. Predict a relationship between atomic radius and electronegativity if you were to graph atomic radii on the *x*-axis and electronegativity values on the *y*-axis. Explain the basis of your prediction.

_____

_____

_____

_____

_____

G Test your prediction in Question 18 by creating a scatterplot showing the atomic radii on the *x*-axis and electronegativity values on the *y*-axis.

19. Does your scatterplot support your prediction in Question 18? Explain.

_____

_____

_____

_____

_____

TABLE 1

Element	Atomic Number	Atomic Radius (pm)	Electronegativity	Electron Affinity (kJ/mol)	First Ionization Energy (eV)
Li	3	145	0.98	60	5.4
Be	4	105	1.57	−50	9.3
B	5	85	2.04	27	8.3
C	6	70	2.55	122	11.3
N	7	65	3.04	−7	14.5
O	8	60	3.44	141	13.6
F	9	50	3.98	328	17.4
Na	11	180	0.93	53	5.1
Mg	12			−40	7.6
Al	13	125	1.61	42	6.0
Si	14	110	1.90	134	8.2
P	15	100	2.19	72	10.5
S	16	100	2.58	200	10.4
Cl	17	100	3.16	349	13.0
K	19	220	0.82	48	4.3
Ca	20	180	1.0	2	6.1
Sc	21	160	1.36	18	6.6
Ti	22	140	1.54	7	6.8
V	23	135	1.63	51	6.7
Cr	24	140	1.66	65	6.8
Mn	25	140	1.55	−50	7.4
Fe	26			15	7.9
Co	27	135	1.88	64	7.9
Ni	28	135	1.91	112	7.6
Cu	29	135	1.90	119	7.7
Zn	30	135	1.65	−60	9.4
Ga	31	130	1.81	41	6.0
Ge	32	125	2.01	119	7.9
Se	34	115		195	9.8
Br	35	115	2.96	325	11.8
Rb	37	235	0.82	47	4.2
Sr	38	200	0.95	5	5.7
Y	39	180	1.22	30	6.2
Zr	40	155	1.33	42	6.6
Nb	41	145	1.6	89	6.8
Mo	42	145	2.16	72	7.1
Tc	43	135	1.9	53	7.3
Ru	44	130	2.2	101	7.4
Rh	45	135	2.28	110	7.5
Pd	46	140	2.20	54	8.3
Ag	47	160	1.93	126	7.6

Element	Atomic Number	Atomic Radius (pm)	Electronegativity	Electron Affinity (kJ/mol)	First Ionization Energy (eV)
Cd	48	155	1.69	−70	9.0
In	49	155	1.78	37	5.8
Sn	50	145	1.96	107	7.3
Sb	51	145	2.05	101	8.6
Te	52	140	2.1	190	9.0
I	53	140	2.66	295	10.5
Cs	55	260	0.79	46	3.9
Ba	56	215	0.89	14	5.2
La	57	195	1.10	53	5.6
Ce	58	185	1.12	55	5.5
Pr	59	185	1.13	93	5.5
Nd	60	185	1.14	185	5.5
Pm	61	185	1.13	12	5.6
Sm	62	185	1.17	16	5.6
Eu	63	185	1.2	11	5.7
Gd	64	180	1.20	13	6.2
Tb	65	175	1.1	112	5.9
Ho	67	175	1.23	33	6.0
Er	68	175	1.24	30	6.1
Tm	69	175	1.25	99	6.2
Yb	70	175	1.1	−2	6.3
Lu	71	175	1.27	23	5.4
Hf	72	155	1.3	17	6.8
Ta	73	145	1.5	31	7.5
W	74	135	2.36	79	7.9
Re	75	135	1.9	6	7.8
Os	76	130	2.2	104	8.4
Ir	77	135	2.20	151	9.0
Pt	78	135	2.28	205	9.0
Au	79	135	2.54	223	9.2
Hg	80	150	2.0	−50	10.4
Tl	81	190	1.62	36	6.1
Pb	82		1.87	34	7.4
Bi	83	160	2.02	91	7.3
Po	84	190	2.0	183	8.4
At	85	115	2.18	78	9.3

Name _____

Date _____

The Name's Bond—Covalent Bond

Modeling Covalent Bonds

Building models of molecules may not be new to you. You may have built such models using toothpicks and colored marshmallows, gumdrops, or foam balls. These models can be useful, but certain aspects of molecular structure can't be modeled well by stiff toothpicks. You'll see that in this lab activity and again in Chapter 8. Molecular modeling sets that are purposefully designed for the task can tell us more about what happens when atoms get together to share electrons. In this lab activity, you'll explore multiple covalent bonds and polarity using one such product—a modeling set made by MolyMod.

Can physical models accurately represent what happens when atoms make covalent bonds?

QUESTIONS

» How do single, double, and triple covalent bonds compare?

» What affects the polarity of covalently bonded molecules?

EQUIPMENT

• MolyMod® modeling set

Procedure

EXPLORING SINGLE, DOUBLE, AND TRIPLE BONDS

MolyMod sets use different-colored balls to represent different elements: black (carbon), red (oxygen), and white (hydrogen). There are also different kinds of connectors for joining atoms together—rigid connectors for single bonds and flexible connectors for multiple bonds.

A Compare the MolyMod carbon, oxygen, and hydrogen atoms.

1. Other than color, describe the differences that you observe between the MolyMod "atoms" of each element.

_____

_____

_____

2. Thinking in terms of atomic structure, what do you suppose the differences that you described in Question 1 represent?

_____

_____

_____

_____

3. Observe the placement of the holes in the oxygen and carbon atoms. What significance will the fixed locations of the holes have for building molecules, and how is this different from, for example, toothpick and marshmallow models?

_____

_____

_____

4. What do the gray connectors in your model represent?

_____

The reasoning behind the locations of the holes in the various MolyMod atoms will be explored in the Chapter 8 material on bond geometry. For now it suffices to know that bonds between real atoms do tend to form in the positions suggested by the MolyMod atoms.

A SIMPLE SINGLE BOND

B Make a model of molecular hydrogen using two hydrogen atoms and a rigid single-bond connector. Leave this model intact for use later in the activity.

5. How many ways are there to build a model of molecular hydrogen using the indicated parts?

_____

6. Is this an accurate representation of what happens when hydrogen bonds with itself? Explain.

_____

_____

_____

_____

COMPARING SINGLE AND MULTIPLE BONDS

C Build a model of ethane (C_2H_6) using the appropriate atoms and single-bond connectors. This model and those that you build in Steps D and F should be left intact for the discussion that follows.

D Build another ethane molecule. Once you finish it, examine it and consider what you would need to do to replace the carbon-carbon bond with a double bond.

7. What do you need to do to your ethane model to form a double bond in it?

_____

_____

_____

_____

E In your second ethane model, replace the single bond with a double bond on the basis of your answer to Question 7. You will need to use the flexible connectors between the carbon atoms. The resulting molecule is *ethene*.

F Now repeat Steps D and E to make a third molecule that contains a triple bond rather than a double bond. This is a molecule of *ethyne*.

Now compare your three models—ethane, ethene, and ethyne—paying particular attention to the bonds.

8. On the basis of bond strength, rank the three compounds from least to most strong and explain why you ranked them in that order.

_____

_____

_____

_____

THINKING ABOUT POLARITY

Now let's consider how physical models such as those built using Moly-Mod sets can help us visualize polarity in molecules.

9. What causes polarity in a covalent molecule?

_____

_____

_____

G Take another look at your model of molecular hydrogen.

10. Is H_2 polar or nonpolar? How does the model show this?

_____

_____

_____

11. Now look at your model of ethane. Are its carbon-hydrogen bonds polar? Explain.

_____

_____

_____

12. Look carefully at your models of ethane, ethene, and ethyne. Are any of them polar molecules? Explain.

_____

_____

_____

H Now remove two of the hydrogen atoms from one carbon atom in your ethane model and replace them with a double-bonded oxygen atom. The resulting molecule is *ethanal*, a compound classified as an *aldehyde*. (You will learn about aldehydes in Chapter 20.)

13. Is ethanal polar? Explain.

_____

_____

_____

_____

14. Would *saturating* your ethanal molecule—by opening one of the pair of bonds in the double bond and adding a hydrogen atom to the oxygen— make the resulting molecule (ethanol) nonpolar? Explain.

_____

_____

_____

Going Further

Ozone, O_3, is a compound formed in the earth's upper atmosphere when ordinary oxygen, O_2, is bombarded by ultraviolet light. The region of the atmosphere where the greatest concentration of ozone occurs is known as the *ozone layer*. The ozone layer helps protect the earth from the harmful effects of UV light by blocking most of the incoming UV rays before they reach the planet's surface.

I Create a model of ozone by connecting three oxygen atoms together using single bonds.

15. Sketch your ozone molecule in the space provided.

Conduct an internet search using the keyword "ozone" to find information about the molecular structure of ozone.

16. Is the structure that you sketched in Question 15 correct? Explain.

_____

_____

_____

_____

17. How does your answer to Question 16 illustrate a shortcoming with the MolyMod system?

_____

_____

_____

_____

_____

_____

18. If the MolyMod system has this particular limitation, why is it still used for modeling? Can you think of any other models that are still used as educational tools despite their limited ability to portray reality? (*Hint*: Think back to Chapter 5.)

_____

_____

_____

_____

_____

_____

_____

_____

Name

Date

Bulletproof Chemistry

Relating Chemical Bonds and Physical Properties

A woman approached a teller one April morning in 2012 at a BB&T bank in Smyrna, Georgia. In the slot under the wall of glass, she passed to the teller a typed demand note. When the teller moved too slowly, the woman pulled a gun and demanded money. Happily, the glass was bulletproof. Eventually, the would-be bank robber left without a dime, foiled by chemistry!

Chemical bonds are responsible for the physical properties of substances such as bulletproof glass. We can use these properties to keep our homes warm, cook our food, and make great running shoes.

How can we use physical properties to identify bond types in substances?

Ionic, covalent, and metallic bonds play a big role in determining the physical properties of substances. If you can observe the physical properties of a substance, you can often determine its bond type. In the table on the next page, notice the properties that each bond type typically produces in substances.

In this lab activity, you will examine the melting point, solubility, and conductivity of several substances in order to determine the types of bonds they contain. These bonds and the properties they create could make the difference in the way your next grilled cheese sandwich turns out or how warm your house stays on a cold day.

QUESTIONS

» How do the properties of compounds relate to their chemical bonds?

» Is there a relationship between the bond types in a compound and its melting point?

» Is there a relationship between the bond types in a compound and its solubility and conductivity?

» How can I identify an unknown substance on the basis of empirical evidence?

EQUIPMENT

- laboratory burner and lighter
- conductivity tester
- ring stand and ring
- wire gauze
- evaporating dish
- test tubes (6)
- test tube rack
- wash bottle with distilled water
- weighing paper
- unknown substances (3)
- acetone

Bulletproof glass is made by putting together two different types of glass. Both are transparent, but one is more flexible than the other. Glass is made mostly of silicon dioxide, a covalent compound with the same formula as sand.

Bond Type / Characteristics	Ionic Bond	Covalent Bond	Metallic Bond
Electrons	transferred	shared between two atoms	free among all atoms
Smallest Unit	formula unit	molecule	atom
Melting Point	high	relatively low	relatively high
Solubility	often soluble in polar solvents but insoluble in nonpolar solvents	soluble in polar solvents if polar covalent; soluble in nonpolar solvents if nonpolar covalent	insoluble in both polar and nonpolar solvents
Conductivity	conducts electricity when melted or dissolved	usually does not conduct electricity	good conductor of electricity

Procedure

MELTING POINTS

A Obtain small samples of the three unknown substances provided by your teacher. Put each sample on a separate piece of weighing paper.

B Set up an apparatus as shown below.

C Place a small amount (about the size of an un-cooked grain of rice) of Unknown 1 in an evaporating dish. Set the dish on the wire gauze and gently heat the contents.

D If the unknown does not readily melt, heat it strongly for a minute or two. Describe how easily the substance melts in Table 1.

E Repeat Steps C and D for Unknowns 2 and 3, and record your observations in Table 1.

1. Using the table in the introduction, rank the types of bonds by increasing bond strength on the basis of melting points.

_____

2. Ionic compounds and metallic compounds have higher melting points than covalent compounds. Why do you think this is so?

_____

_____

_____

_____

3. On the basis of your observations, make a hypothesis about which unknown has metallic bonds, which has ionic bonds, and which has covalent bonds before you proceed with more testing.

_____

_____

_____

_____

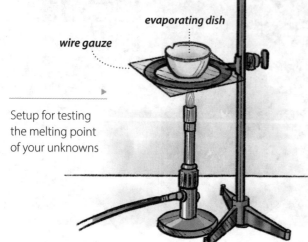

evaporating dish

wire gauze

Setup for testing the melting point of your unknowns

SOLUBILITY

F Try to dissolve Unknown 1 by placing a small amount of the substance (about the size of an uncooked grain of rice) in a test tube and adding distilled water to fill the test tube one-quarter full. Record the relative solubility in Table 1. You'll need this sample for the conductivity test, so don't discard it! You may want to label your test tube.

G Repeat Step F for relative solubility with Unknowns 2 and 3. Record your observations in Table 1.

4. Is water a polar or a nonpolar liquid?

_____

One general rule about dissolving substances is that "like dissolves like," meaning that polar liquids tend to dissolve polar substances, and that nonpolar liquids tend to dissolve nonpolar substances. This will be discussed in more detail in Chapter 14.

5. Would water be more likely to dissolve ionic or covalent compounds? Explain.

_____

_____

_____

_____

Before you continue with the second part of the procedure, ***make sure that no one in the laboratory has a laboratory burner lit.*** You will be using acetone, a nonpolar liquid used in fingernail polish remover, and it is extremely flammable! You will not need a laboratory burner for the rest of this activity.

H Repeat Step F for each unknown using acetone as the solvent. Record your observations in Table 1.

6. Acetone is a nonpolar liquid. Is it more likely to dissolve ionic or covalent compounds? Explain.

_____

_____

_____

_____

7. On the basis of your observations, make a hypothesis about which unknown is metallic, which is ionic, and which is covalent before you proceed with more testing.

_____

_____

_____

_____

CONDUCTIVITY

Now you will test to see whether your unknowns allow electricity to pass through them easily, a property known as *conductivity*.

I Lower the two electrodes of the conductivity tester (see right) into the aqueous solution for Unknown 1. If the sample is conductive, the light will illuminate. Record your observations in Table 1.

J Using the wash bottle, rinse the electrodes with distilled water and then dry the electrodes.

K Repeat Steps I and J for the remaining five test tubes.

L Test the conductivity of the remaining small amounts of each unknown solid by touching the electrodes to each one. Again, rinse and dry the probes between each test. Record your observations in Table 1.

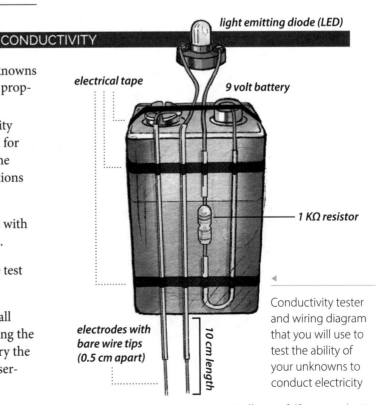

light emitting diode (LED)

electrical tape

9 volt battery

1 KΩ resistor

electrodes with bare wire tips (0.5 cm apart)

10 cm length

Conductivity tester and wiring diagram that you will use to test the ability of your unknowns to conduct electricity

Analysis

8. Identify the bond type in each of your three unknowns. Check with your teacher to learn the identities of the unknowns and to see whether your hypotheses are correct.

_____

_____

9. Did the substances that you used in this lab activity follow the "like dissolves like" rule? Explain.

_____

_____

10. Did the "solution" that you formed by mixing the metal and water conduct electricity? How do your results compare with those for the solid metal?

_____

11. Why does an ionic solid conduct electricity only in the molten state or in solution?

_____

_____

Going Further

12. Imagine that ionic compounds such as table salt did *not* dissolve in water. How would that affect your life?

_____

_____

_____

_____

13. Think of some ways that we can create substances with customized physical properties for special uses, like airplane wings, electric wires, and insulation for homes.

_____

_____

14. Considering what you wrote in Question 13, explain how God uses chemists to provide for our needs.

_____

_____

_____

_____

_____

_____

TABLE 1 *Properties of Unknown Substances*

	Unknown 1	Unknown 2	Unknown 3
Melting			
Solubility in Water (H$_2$O)			
Solubility in Acetone (CH$_3$COCH$_3$)			
Conductivity of Aqueous Mixtures			
Conductivity of Acetone Mixtures			
Conductivity of the Solids			

Name _____

Date _____

EQUIPMENT

- foam balls, 7.5 cm (9)
- foam balls, 2.5 cm (29)
- toothpicks (36)

The Shape of Things

Modeling Molecules

Scale models are helpful to show the important features of an object. We use scale models for both large and small objects. We scale large objects down so that we can look at the entire object at a glance. These scaled-down models include model cars, trains, and ships, models of the solar system, and models of buildings. The specific scale that we use depends on the size of the actual object and the size of model that we want to make. For models of cars it is common to use a scale of 1:25; that is, 1 cm on the model represents 25 cm on the actual car. For ships, you would need a smaller scale, such as 1:200. Of course, if you were making a tabletop model of the solar system, you would need a tiny scale—1:1.5×10^{13}.

What determines the shape of a molecule?

When we study objects that are very small, such as molecules, we need scaled-up models. You may have done this before in a biology class, for example, when making a model of a cell. In this lab activity you will make scaled-up models of molecules. This is a very large-scale model because 1 cm on your models will represent 2×10^{-9} cm in a real-world molecule.

In this lab activity you will make physical three-dimensional models of molecules. These models will give you the opportunity to make connections between the Lewis structures that you have been drawing in class and the three-dimensional molecules that they represent.

QUESTIONS

» How do I draw Lewis structures of molecules?

» How do I make 3D models of molecules?

» How does the shape of a molecule affect its polarity?

Procedure

Consider formaldehyde (CH$_2$O). To make a model of this organic compound, we begin by drawing its Lewis structure.

$$\begin{array}{c} H \\ \end{array} \diagdown \diagup C = \ddot{O}\!\!:$$

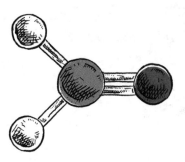

After drawing the Lewis dot structure, we observe that carbon is the central atom. It has three regions of electrons around it, two single bonds and a double bond, the double bond acting as a single region of electrons. Each of the single bonds connects a hydrogen atom with the central carbon atom, and the double bond connects the carbon atom with the oxygen atom.

It's possible to make a model showing three regions of electrons that are spaced as far apart as possible. This molecule is trigonal planar—the bonds lie in the same plane and point to the three corners of a triangle. By comparing electronegativity values, you can determine that the molecule contains polar bonds and that the molecule is polar overall.

Now it's your turn to explore some molecular models. To begin with, let's look at some of the basic possible shapes.

DETERMINING BOND ANGLE

A Take two of the large foam balls, representing central atoms, and insert two toothpicks, representing electrons, either bonding or unbonded, into each ball so that the toothpicks are as far from each other as possible. What is the approximate angle between the toothpicks? Record this bond angle in Table 1.

B Repeat Step A, but use three large foam balls and insert three toothpicks in each.

C Repeat Step A, but use four large foam balls and insert four toothpicks in each.

1. What determines the bond angles in each of your models? Explain how Steps A–C demonstrate this fact.

_____

_____

_____

_____

_____

_____

DETERMINING BASIC SHAPES

D To the first foam ball from Step A attach one small foam ball to one of the toothpicks, representing an atom bonded to the central atom. To the second large foam ball, attach a small foam ball to each of the toothpicks. What shape would you call each of these molecules? Record your observations in Table 1.

E Repeat Step D for the three large foam balls from Step B, adding one, two, and three small foam balls to each of the molecules.

F Repeat Step D for the four large foam balls from Step C, adding one, two, three, and then four small foam balls to each of the molecules.

G Disassemble your models so that you can use the parts to model real molecules.

MODELING ACTUAL MOLECULES

H Table 2 includes the molecules that you will now model. Begin by drawing the Lewis structure for each molecule in Table 2.

I Count the regions of electrons around each central atom. A bond counts as one region, regardless of whether it is a single or multiple bond, and each lone pair counts as one region. Record your counts in Table 2.

2. What do you notice about the number of valence electrons for elements that are usually central atoms?

_____

_____

_____

J Identify how many atoms are bonded to each central atom and record your counts in Table 2.

K Now let's make some models, starting with formaldehyde. Again, use the large foam balls for the central atom, the toothpicks for regions of electrons, and small foam balls for outer atoms. Record the finished molecule's shape in Table 2.

L Identify any polar bonds in your molecule. Remember that when two different atoms are bonded together, the bond is polar. Record your observations in Table 2.

3. In the formaldehyde molecule on page 66, why do carbon and hydrogen form a slightly polar bond?

_____

_____

_____

M Study the shape of your molecule and the locations of any polar bonds to determine whether the entire molecule is polar. Record your conclusions in Table 2.

N Repeat Steps K–M for the additional molecules listed in Table 2. Be sure to read ahead—some of the following questions pertain to a particular model.

4. Consider the model for methane. If carbon and hydrogen form a slightly polar bond, why is methane nonpolar?

_____

_____

_____

5. If you were to add a hydrogen ion (H⁺) to the ammonia model that you made, what substance would you have? Would the additional hydrogen ion cause the shape of the new molecule to be different from ammonia? Explain.

_____

_____

_____

6. On the basis of your answer to Question 5, do you think that the addition of a hydrogen ion (H⁺) would change the polar nature of ammonia? Explain.

_____

_____

_____

7. What is the difference between the carbon-oxygen bond in your model of methanol and the one found in carbon dioxide?

_____

_____

_____

Suppose that two students who are working through this lab activity show you their Lewis structures for dichloromethane. The first student explains that her Lewis structure (below left) demonstrates that the molecule is polar because the polar chlorine-carbon bonds and polar hydrogen-carbon bonds pull electrons unequally. The second student claims that his Lewis structure (below right) demonstrates that the molecule is nonpolar because the pulls of the two chlorine atoms balance, as do the pulls of the two hydrogen atoms, leaving a balanced, nonpolar molecule.

$$
\begin{array}{ccc}
\text{Cl} & & \text{H} \\
| & & | \\
\text{Cl}-\text{C}-\text{H} & & \text{Cl}-\text{C}-\text{Cl} \\
| & & | \\
\text{H} & & \text{H}
\end{array}
$$

8. Use what you learned from your three-dimensional model to explain the polarity of this molecule.

_____

_____

_____

_____

_____

9. On the basis of what you have observed, state which molecular shape(s) will *always* produce polar molecules when the central atom is bonded to an atom (or atoms) of a different element.

_____

_____

_____

10. Which molecular shape(s) will produce nonpolar molecules if a central carbon atom is bonded to atoms of a different element?

_____

_____

_____

TABLE 1 *Molecular Shapes*

Number of Electron Regions	Bond Angle	Nuclei around Central Atom	Geometry
2		1	
		2	
3		1	
		2	
		3	
4		1	
		2	
		3	
		4	

TABLE 2

IUPAC Name and Formula	Formalde-hyde CH_2O	Methane CH_4	Water H_2O	Ammonia NH_3	Carbon Dioxide CO_2	Methanol CH_3OH	Hydridoni-tridocarbon HCN	Dichloro-methane CH_2Cl_2	Carbon Tetrachloride CCl_4
Lewis Structure									
Regions of Electrons around Central Atom									
Atoms around Central Atom									
Molecular Shape									
Polar Bonds?									
Polar Molecule?									

Change of Address

Investigating Molecular Orbitals

One of the great challenges of chemistry is the fact that almost everything we are studying is too small to see, even with magnification. To understand what is going on inside atoms and molecules, scientists observe how matter interacts with its surroundings and then hypothesize about what is happening at the atomic and molecular levels. You can understand why the concept of modeling is so important in chemistry.

QUESTIONS

» How do I model molecular orbitals?

» How does molecular orbital theory explain that so few elements are found unbonded in nature?

EQUIPMENT

• none

How does the molecular orbital theory relate to orbital notation for atoms?

In the last few chapters in your textbook you have been learning about the structure of atoms, with much of your time spent learning about where the electrons are located and what they are doing. The electrons, particularly the valence electrons, are key actors in chemical reactions and chemical bonding. In this lab activity, you will look more closely at the molecular orbital theory, which postulates that the electrons in the atoms can move between atomic orbitals. You might say that they experience a change of address. Let's see what the molecular orbital theory says about the valence electrons in a molecule.

According to the molecular orbital theory, all the valence electrons from bonded atoms become delocalized from their atomic orbitals and relocate to newly formed molecular orbitals. This theory helps us understand why some atoms bond, while other atoms do not. Molecular orbital theory can also explain why some atoms bond with stronger double and triple bonds. One of the most amazing things about this model is that it accurately predicts the magnetic behavior of bonded substances. But let's not get ahead of ourselves!

Procedure

Let's start by looking at a simple example, H_2. We draw the orbital notation for each of the hydrogen atoms that will form H_2.

Hydrogen 1 $\quad \dfrac{\uparrow}{1s} \quad\quad\quad \dfrac{\uparrow}{1s} \quad$ *Hydrogen 2*

Since each hydrogen atom contributes an orbital, there will be two molecular orbitals in H_2. We draw the two orbitals in between the atomic orbitals of the hydrogen atoms. Just like atomic orbitals, molecular orbitals have different energy levels. When drawing molecular orbitals, we indicate the lower energy orbitals by placing them at the bottom of the diagram. Therefore, starting at the bottom we have a σ1s orbital. The Greek letter *sigma*, σ, indicates that the electrons in this orbital will bond via a sigma bond. The 1s indicates that this orbital formed from the 1s orbitals of the bonding atoms. The σ1s orbital is a bonding orbital—one that works toward successful bonding of the atoms. The second molecular orbital is designated σ1s* and is located above the first orbital because it is a higher energy orbital. The asterisk indicates that this is an antibonding orbital and actually works against the atoms' attempt at bonding. Let's take a look at these orbitals.

Hydrogen 1 $\quad \dfrac{\uparrow}{1s} \quad\quad \dfrac{\overline{}}{\sigma\,1s*} \quad \dfrac{\uparrow}{1s} \quad$ *Hydrogen 2*

$$\dfrac{\overline{}}{\sigma\,1s}$$

Notice that the σ1s orbital is lower than the atomic orbitals, indicating a lower energy state, while the nonbonding orbital is above the atomic orbitals—a higher energy state.

Now we need to put electrons in the orbitals. Again, just like with atomic orbitals, we always fill lower energy orbitals first. Therefore, the electron from each atom will fill the σ1s orbital. Our finalized diagram is shown below.

Hydrogen 1 $\quad \dfrac{\uparrow}{1s} \quad\quad \dfrac{\overline{}}{\sigma\,1s*} \quad \dfrac{\uparrow}{1s} \quad$ *Hydrogen 2*

$$\dfrac{\uparrow\downarrow}{\sigma\,1s}$$

What does this diagram tell us? From it, we can tell whether the molecule is stable; if so, it will likely form and stay together. Stability is dependent on the number of electrons in bonding orbitals versus the number of electrons in nonbonding orbitals. To determine stability, we calculate the bond order.

$$BO = \frac{\text{electrons in bonding orbitals} - \text{electrons in antibonding orbitals}}{2}$$

For our hydrogen molecule we calculate the bond order to be 1.

$$BO = \frac{2 - 0}{2} = 1$$

Any bond order greater than 0 indicates a stable, likely-to-form molecule. Also notice that there are no unpaired electrons in the molecular orbitals. This tells chemists that the material is likely to be nonmagnetic, or *diamagnetic*. If there were any unpaired electrons, the material would be attracted to magnets; that is, it would be *paramagnetic*.

A Use Drawing Area 1 to draw the orbital notation for each of two helium atoms that attempt to form He_2. As you become more comfortable with drawing molecular orbital diagrams, you will be able to skip this step.

1. How many total atomic orbitals are there in the two helium atoms? What does this tell us about the number of molecular orbitals in He_2?

_____

_____

_____

B Draw the molecular orbitals for the He_2.

C Add the electrons to the molecular orbitals.

D Determine the bond order and indicate whether it is stable or unstable and paramagnetic or diamagnetic. Record your observations with your drawings.

E Using Drawing Area 1, repeat Steps A–D for H_2^-. Don't forget the extra electron that gives it a charge of 1−.

MOLECULAR ORBITALS FOR THE SECOND ENERGY LEVEL

The molecular orbital diagrams that we have considered so far have been fairly simple. How do the diagrams change once we are in the second energy level, with its s and p suborbitals? Let's look at the molecular orbital diagram for C_2.

We start by drawing the orbital notation for each of the carbon atoms that will form C_2, but we include only the orbitals from energy level 2 since that is where carbon's valence electrons are.

Carbon 1 $\underset{2s}{\uparrow\downarrow}$ $\underset{2p}{\uparrow \ \uparrow \ \underline{}}$ $\underset{2s}{\uparrow\downarrow}$ $\underset{2p}{\uparrow \ \uparrow \ \underline{}}$ Carbon 2

Each carbon atom has four orbitals; therefore the C_2 molecule will have eight molecular orbitals, four bonding and four nonbonding. Starting at the bottom, we have the σ2s, and σ2s*, a pair of π2p orbitals, and a σ2p orbital. We finish with a pair of π2p* orbitals and a σ2p* orbital. The p orbitals are often designated with x, y, and z subscripts to signify the three dimensional axes. As in the earlier orbital diagrams, the nonbonding orbitals are at a higher energy state than their associated bonding orbitals. A note about the order of the orbitals is important to state here: The arrangement shown here works for boron, carbon, and nitrogen; when dealing with oxygen, fluorine, or neon, the π2p orbitals and the σ2p orbital are reversed.

$\underset{2s}{\uparrow\downarrow}$ $\underset{2p}{\uparrow \ \uparrow \ \underline{}}$ $\overline{\pi\ 2p_x^{\ *}}$ $\overline{\sigma\ 2p_z^{\ *}}$ $\overline{\pi\ 2p_y^{\ *}}$ $\underset{2s}{\uparrow\downarrow}$ $\underset{2p}{\uparrow \ \uparrow \ \underline{}}$

$\overline{\pi\ 2p_x}$ $\overline{\sigma\ 2p_z}$ $\overline{\pi\ 2p_y}$

Carbon 1 $\overline{\sigma\ 2s^*}$ **Carbon 2**

$\overline{\sigma\ 2s}$

Filling the orbitals is very much like drawing atomic orbital notation. Fill lower energy levels first, adding one electron to each orbital prior to adding a second electron to any of them. Electrons in any particular orbital must have opposite spins.

We calculate the bond order for dicarbon to be 2.

$$BO = \frac{6 - 2}{2} = 2$$

The bond order of 2 indicates that the molecule is stable. There is also a relationship between bond order and multiple bonds. While not a hard and fast rule, the relationship does hold true for dicarbon. Dicarbon has a bond order of 2 and indeed does have a double bond in it. We can also see that, since there are no lone electrons in dicarbon, it is diamagnetic.

F Using Drawing Area 1, repeat Steps A–D for for Li_2, Be_2, O_2^-, and N_2.

MOLECULAR ORBITALS FOR MOLECULES WITH DISSIMILAR ATOMS

Up to this point we have looked only at diatomic molecules that contain two of the same type atom. Now let's consider the molecular orbital diagrams for a molecule made of two different atoms. We'll start by drawing the molecular orbital diagram for boron monofluoride (BF), beginning by drawing the orbital notation for each of its atoms.

Notice that the orbitals for fluorine are lower than those for boron. Due to

fluorine's higher electronegativity, those orbitals are lower in energy than boron's orbitals are.

Because the molecule includes fluorine, we use the molecule orbital order for fluorine. We then fill the orbitals with electrons.

The bond order for boron monofluoride is 3.

$$BO = \frac{8 - 2}{2} = 3$$

This indicates that the molecule is very stable and may have a triple bond. A look at one possible Lewis structure for boron monofluoride confirms that a triple bond is possible.

$$:B \equiv F:$$

Again, there are no lone electrons in boron monofluoride, so it is diamagnetic.

G Using Drawing Area 2, repeat Steps A–D for CO, NO, CN⁻, and OF⁺.

2. Very few substances are found in nature as individual atoms. According to molecular orbital theory, particularly bond order, does it make sense that most substances naturally exist as bonded molecules rather than individual atoms? Explain.

_____

_____

_____

_____

_____

_____

H_2^-		He_2	
Bond Order?		**Bond Order?**	
Stable?		**Stable?**	
Magnetism?		**Magnetism?**	

Li_2		Be_2	
Bond Order?		**Bond Order?**	
Stable?		**Stable?**	
Magnetism?		**Magnetism?**	

O_2^-		N_2	
Bond Order?		**Bond Order?**	
Stable?		**Stable?**	
Magnetism?		**Magnetism?**	

DRAWING AREA 2

CO		NO	
Bond Order?		**Bond Order?**	
Stable?		**Stable?**	
Magnetism?		**Magnetism?**	

CN⁻		OF⁺	
Bond Order?		**Bond Order?**	
Stable?		**Stable?**	
Magnetism?		**Magnetism?**	

Name _____

Date _____

EQUIPMENT

- compound name and formula cards
- compound names and formulas worksheet

Compounds Scavenger Hunt

Naming Chemical Compounds

Do you have a hobby? Most people do. And most hobbies come with a lot of jargon—words that mean something to people inside the hobby but might sound like gibberish to everyone else. For instance, do the terms *frontside air*, *Haakon flip*, or *switchstance* mean anything to you? They probably do if you are into snowboarding. If they don't, you probably are not deeply immersed into snowboarding culture. The names of chemical compounds are similar—the more chemistry you do, the more second nature compound names become. In this activity you are going to be given ample opportunity to practice naming compounds and writing formulas. This activity will pay dividends as you start studying chemical reactions and equations in the next chapter.

How do I name chemical compounds?

1. When looking at a chemical formula, what are some questions that you can ask that will help identify the type of compound as an acid, covalent compound, ionic compound that doesn't use the Stock system, or an ionic compound that *does* use the Stock system?

   _____

   _____

   _____

   _____

   _____

QUESTIONS

» How do I write the chemical formulas for compounds on the basis of their names?

» How do I name chemical compounds on the basis of their formulas?

2. When looking at a chemical name, what are some questions that you can ask that will help identify the type of compound as an acid, covalent compound, ionic compound that doesn't use the Stock system, or an ionic compound that *does* use the Stock system?

_____

_____

_____

Procedure

Though you are working in teams, each team member should do all the problems. Teammates should help each other work through naming compounds and writing formulas. If you get stuck, see what your teammate thinks. If you are both stuck, see what your classmates and teacher think.

A Complete the table on pages 81–85. In each row you are given either the name or the formula for a compound. Identify the type of compound as either an acid (A), a covalent compound (C), an ionic non-Stock system compound (I), or an ionic Stock system compound (S). Then give the missing formula or name for that compound.

B When you think you have the names and formulas correct, check your work in the scavenger hunt. The solutions are printed on cards around the room. The cards are grouped by type of compound. Work your way around the room to find the card with each compound. On the card is a card number; record this in the appropriate column of the table.

C If you can't find a card with the desired compound, double-check the type and formula/name. Consider discussing with other groups or your teacher the ones that you are having difficulty with.

Analysis

3. Which were the most difficult compounds to name? Explain.

_____

_____

_____

4. Which were the most difficult compounds to write formulas for? Explain.

_____

_____

_____

Compound Names and Formulas

Given Name or Formula	Type	Answer: Name or Formula	Card Number
aluminum oxide			
NO			
iron(II) iodide			
MgS			
H_3BO_3			
LiBr			
nitrogen trifluoride			
sodium dihydrogen phosphate			
chromic acid			
$SrCl_2$			
tin(IV) sulfide			
sodium iodide			
$NaHCO_3$			
phosphoric acid			
CBr_4			
hydroiodic acid			
aluminum phosphide			
$HClO_4$			
Ag_2CO_3			
phosphorus trichloride			
$Al(OH)_3$			

Given Name or Formula	Type	Answer: Name or Formula	Card Number
calcium oxide			
$HClO_1$			
K_2HPO_4			
$Ca(ClO_3)_2$			
SnF_2			
nitrous acid			
$Mn(NO_3)_2$			
hydrofluoric acid			
Al_2S_3			
carbonic acid			
carbon dioxide			
magnesium hydride			
H_3PO_3			
nitrogen dioxide			
$KMnO_4$			
magnesium nitride			
carbon monoxide			
ammonium nitrate			
magnesium hydroxide			
sodium oxalate			
sodium chromate			

Given Name or Formula	Type	Answer: Name or Formula	Card Number
sulfur hexafluoride			
$HgBr_2$			
AlN			
$Ca(C_2H_3O_2)_2$			
H_2SO_3			
sulfur trioxide			
NaClO			
$RaBr_2$			
calcium carbonate			
strontium fluoride			
lead(II) phosphate			
barium cyanide			
mercury(II) oxide			
copper(I) fluoride			
sulfuric acid			
iron(III) oxide			
tungsten(V) bromide			
SnS			
tin(IV) iodide			
$FeCl_2$			
KI			

Given Name or Formula	Type	Answer: Name or Formula	Card Number
Co_3P_2			
$HClO_2$			
copper(II) sulfide			
xenon hexafluoride			
potassium sulfate			
magnesium sulfide			
potassium nitrite			
CO			
HBr			
Cu_2S			
NI_3			
aluminum phosphate			
dinitrogen monoxide			
lithium sulfide			
iodic acid			
AuI			
XeO_3			
tin(II) chloride			
PbI_2			
radium chloride			
PBr_7			

Given Name or Formula	Type	Answer: Name or Formula	Card Number
potassium bromate			
Li_2CO_3			
Na_2S			
$Mg(HCO_3)_2$			
HCN			
nitric acid			
Ca_3N_2			
Cr_2O_3			
SF_4			
$HClO_3$			
N_2O_3			
MgO			
hydrosulfuric acid			
$HC_2H_3O_2$			
S_4N_4			
P_2F_4			

Expeditions in Chemical Equations

Investigating Chemical Reactions and Equations

Many people love soda; in fact, in 2018 the average American drank almost thirty-nine gallons of it. But as much as they love the sweetness, many would like to avoid the Calories. So soft drink manufacturers have turned to chemistry to find sweeteners without the Calories.

Today you can get drinks sweetened with aspartame, saccharin, cyclamate, or sucralose with all the sweetness but with no Calories. Each of these sweeteners has gone through a chemical process to produce it. In most cases the process involves a number of chemical reactions. For example, to produce saccharin, chemists react toluene with nitrous acid. The product of this reaction is then reacted with sulfur dioxide. A third reaction combines the product of the second reaction with chlorine and ammonia, resulting in saccharine.

You will do something similar in this lab activity as you start with copper and then conduct a series of four reactions. You will see a number of evidences for chemical reactions and observe a number of the different types of reactions that you have learned about in class.

How can I tell whether a chemical reaction has occurred?

QUESTIONS

» How do I know whether a chemical change occurred?

» How can I differentiate types of chemical reactions?

» How do I model chemical reactions?

EQUIPMENT

- laboratory balance
- laboratory burner and lighter
- crucible tongs
- beaker, 150 mL
- graduated cylinders, 25 mL (2)
- glass stirring rod
- filtering funnel
- clay triangle
- ring stand and ring
- filter paper
- beaker, 250 mL
- pipette
- wire gauze
- copper wool
- sulfuric acid (H_2SO_4), 1 M
- sodium hydroxide (NaOH), 3 M
- goggles
- laboratory apron
- nitrile gloves

Procedure

REACTION 1

A Measure about 1 g of copper wool and form it into a loose wad.

B Set up the Bunsen burner. Light the burner and adjust the flame.

C Using the crucible tongs, hold the copper in the Bunsen burner flame for about 5 minutes. A black product results from the reaction of copper with atmospheric oxygen.

D Place the blackened copper into the 150 mL beaker.

1. Describe anything that you observed during the reaction.

_____

_____

2. Write the balanced chemical equation for Reaction 1 in which copper and atmospheric oxygen combine to form a single product. (*Hint*: Copper in this compound has a +2 oxidation number.)

_____

3. What type(s) of reaction is this first reaction?

_____

4. What compound is formed in this reaction?

_____

5. Copper reacts spontaneously with oxygen in the air. Why do you think the instructions include heating the copper?

_____

_____

_____

REACTION 2

E Pour 20 mL of 1 M H_2SO_4 into a 25 mL graduated cylinder.

F Add the sulfuric acid to the beaker with the black product from Reaction 1 and carefully stir the mixture with the glass stirring rod. You may need to give this solution a minute or two to react.

6. Describe anything that you observed during the reaction.

_____

_____

_____

G Place the filtering funnel in the clay triangle and set it on the ring. Fold a piece of filter paper and place it in the funnel. Consult Appendix C for procedural guidelines if needed.

H Adjust the height of the filtering apparatus so that the tip of the funnel is touching the inside of the beaker. Filter the solution into the 250 mL beaker and save the filtrate in the beaker for the next step. The filter paper containing any unreacted material from Step F can be thrown out.

7. What was the color of the solution after the sulfuric acid was added to the black compound and the resulting solution was filtered?

_____

8. Write the balanced equation for Reaction 2 resulting from the addition of sulfuric acid to the black compound.

_____

9. What type(s) of reaction is the reaction in Question 8?

_____

_____

10. What ion do you think caused the color change in the solution of sulfuric acid and the black compound? What evidence do you have for your answer?

_____

_____

_____

_____

_____

REACTION 3

▐ Pour approximately 20 mL of 3 M NaOH into the second 25 mL graduated cylinder.

▐ Add 10 mL of the sodium hydroxide from the graduated cylinder to the filtrate in the beaker gradually as you stir the mixture with the glass stirring rod. A precipitate will form.

▐ Using a pipette, gradually add sodium hydroxide, stirring continuously until no more precipitate forms.

11. Describe anything that you observed during the reaction.

_____

_____

12. Write the balanced equation for Reaction 3 resulting from the addition of sodium hydroxide to the colored filtrate.

_____

13. What type(s) of reaction is the reaction in Question 12?

_____

WATCH OUT
FOR SPLATTERS!

Make sure that you are wearing gloves, goggles, and an apron when you handle this caustic solution. If it splatters and lands on your skin, it could cause a chemical burn. If this happens, go to your teacher, who can rinse the area with a boric acid solution that will neutralize the base so that it will stop stinging and burning your skin.

REACTION 4

▐ Place the wire gauze on the iron ring. Place the beaker containing the mixture from Reaction 3 on the gauze and *cautiously* heat the mixture until it boils. Stir constantly until a reaction takes place, keeping in mind that **alkaline solutions tend to splatter!**

14. When you heated the mixture, what compound from Reaction 3 changed into copper(II) oxide (CuO) and water?

_____

15. Describe anything that you observed during the reaction.

_____

_____

_____

16. Write the balanced equation for Reaction 4 that resulted in the products copper(II) oxide and water.

_____

17. What type(s) of reaction is the reaction in Question 16?

_____

M Pour the remaining mixture into the waste container provided.

18. What substance(s) was (were) present in your mixture from Reaction 3 that did not react in Reaction 4?

_____

_____

19. If you had filtered out the precipitate produced in Reaction 3, would you have gotten the same results when heating the filtrate? Explain.

_____

_____

_____

_____

20. Compare the result from Reaction 4 to the result from Reaction 1. Did you observe any similarities in these two substances?

_____

_____

21. How can chemical reactions like the four that you have just done be useful to people?

_____

_____

_____

_____

_____

10B LAB

Name _____

Date _____

EQUIPMENT

- reaction plate
- testing solutions
- goggles
- laboratory apron
- nitrile gloves

With a Chance of Precipitation

Inquiring into Solubility

For years, the lack of any eyewitnesses resulted in many crimes going unsolved. As science has advanced, it has helped police departments solve many such challenging cases through DNA evidence. One method for obtaining sufficient DNA is called *ethanol precipitation*. When a scientist adds ethanol to a DNA-containing solution, the DNA comes out of solution and gives the scientist more DNA with which to make an identification.

How can we generate solubility rules for ionic compounds?

Precipitation is one of the indicators that a chemical reaction has occurred. In this inquiry lab activity, you will develop microscale (small-scale) chemistry procedures to develop solubility rules for some common anions and cations in certain given solutions.

QUESTIONS

» How do I know whether a reaction occurred between two solutions?

» How were solubility rules developed?

» How can I model reactions between ions in double-replacement reactions?

Procedure

You are to test combinations of anions and cations from the following two lists so that you can determine the solubility for different ions.

Solution List 1	Solution List 2
aluminum nitrate, $Al(NO_3)_3$	sodium carbonate, Na_2CO_3
ammonium nitrate, NH_4NO_3	sodium chloride, $NaCl$
barium nitrate, $Ba(NO_3)_2$	sodium hydroxide, $NaOH$
calcium nitrate, $Ca(NO_3)_2$	sodium iodide, NaI
copper(II) nitrate, $Cu(NO_3)_2$	sodium phosphate, Na_3PO_4
iron(III) nitrate, $Fe(NO_3)_3$	sodium sulfate, Na_2SO_4
silver nitrate, $AgNO_3$	
zinc nitrate, $Zn(NO_3)_2$	

1. Which list represents the cations that you are testing? Which represents the anions? Explain how you know this.

_____

_____

_____

_____

A Research the types of reactions in Chapter 10 of your textbook. Determine which one or ones relate to solubility and how you will know whether a reaction took place for this type (or these types) of reactions.

B Consider the reaction plate and the two lists of substances to be tested. Brainstorm how you can test all the possible combinations of cations and anions.

C With your lab group, brainstorm ways to organize your data to determine the solubility rules for the cations and anions tested.

D Write specific questions related to precipitation reactions, solubility rules, and microscale chemistry that you could answer by collecting data.

E Write procedures to conduct microscale reactions with all the possible combinations of cation-containing compounds with every anion-containing compound to answer the questions that you formulated in Step D above.

F Have your teacher approve your procedures.

CONDUCTING SCIENTIFIC INVESTIGATIONS

G Following the procedures that you have written, collect the data to answer the questions that you wrote.

DEVELOPING MODELS

H From the data that you collected, make note of trends regarding which combinations of anions and cations reacted and which didn't. Note any exceptions to these general trends. Also note similarities in these trends within chemical groups.

I Develop solubility rules for the anions and cations that you tested, including appropriate exceptions to the rules.

SCIENTIFIC ARGUMENTATION

J Compare your solubility rules with those in your textbook.

K State a claim about the effectiveness of your procedures and support your claim with evidence from your data.

2. Pick three of the combinations that reacted and write the chemical equation, the complete ionic equation, and the net ionic equation for each.

Name _____

Date _____

EQUIPMENT

- laboratory burner and lighter
- laboratory balance
- crucible and cover
- ring stand and ring
- clay triangle
- crucible tongs
- wire gauze
- transfer pipette
- sandpaper
- magnesium ribbon (30 cm)
- goggles
- laboratory apron
- nitrile gloves

Torching Metals

Determining Empirical Formulas

The law of definite composition states that the ratio of elements in a compound is constant for every particle of that compound. These ratios can be expressed by formulas. For example, the compound potassium chlorate is always made up of a ratio of one potassium atom to one chlorine atom to three oxygen atoms, or 1:1:3. We express this in the formula $KClO_3$. Since this formula expresses the simplest whole-number ratio for potassium chlorate, it is potassium chlorate's *empirical formula*. Sometimes a compound's empirical formula is the same as its molecular formula, as with potassium chlorate and water. But in other instances they are different, as in glucose (molecular formula $C_6H_{12}O_6$, empirical formula CH_2O).

In this lab activity, you will synthesize magnesium oxide and experimentally determine its empirical formula.

How can burning a substance make it heavier?

QUESTIONS

» What does the law of definite composition tell me about chemical reactions?

» How can I analyze the composition of a compound?

» How are empirical formulas determined?

Procedure

A. Check your crucible for cracks or chips. Clean your crucible and crucible cover with a damp paper towel. Support them on a ring with a clay triangle. The crucible cover should be tilted on the top of the crucible, leaving a small opening (see below).

From this point forward, handle the crucible and its cover with the crucible tongs!

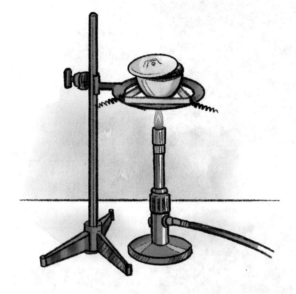

B. Use the laboratory burner to heat the crucible and its cover until they are dry. Allow the crucible to cool until it is comfortable to the touch.

C. Using the crucible tongs, move the crucible and cover to the laboratory balance. Measure the mass of the crucible and cover, and record your data in Table 1.

D. Fold a piece of sandpaper in half. Then, holding the sandpaper so that it opens away from you, clean a strip of magnesium ribbon approximately 30 cm long by gently pulling it through the sandpaper to remove any oxide coating. Wipe it off with a dry paper towel.

1. Why is it necessary to remove any existing oxide coating from the magnesium ribbon before performing the experiment?

_____

_____

_____

_____

_____

E. While wearing gloves, roll up the magnesium ribbon into a tight spiral and place it flat on the bottom of the crucible. It's important that the magnesium be heated uniformly so that it reacts completely.

F. Replace the cover on the crucible and find the mass of the crucible, cover, and magnesium. Record your data in Table 1.

G. Calculate the mass of magnesium and record your answer in Table 1.

H. Place the crucible and its contents on the clay triangle and begin heating them. Heat the magnesium uncovered, but hold the crucible cover nearby with your tongs. Use it only to stop flare-ups and to keep the magnesium burning in a controlled way. ***The moment the magnesium starts to burn, place the cover on the crucible.***

I. Continue heating the magnesium until the magnesium fails to glow. At this point, heat the covered crucible as hot as possible for several additional minutes.

2. Why do you want to keep the cover off to the maximum extent? Why do we cover the magnesium when it starts to burn?

_____

_____

_____

_____

J Using the crucible tongs, carefully move the crucible to the wire gauze. Allow the covered crucible to cool for about 10 minutes.

3. Write the balanced equation for the reaction of magnesium with oxygen gas to form magnesium oxide. What do you predict will be the empirical formula of magnesium oxide?

_____

_____

Air is a mixture of mostly nitrogen and oxygen gases. When magnesium burns in air, most of the magnesium combines with oxygen to form magnesium oxide, but some of the magnesium combines with nitrogen to form magnesium nitride (Mg_3N_2). So what you have in your crucible right now is a mixture of magnesium oxide and magnesium nitride. We need it all to be magnesium oxide.

4. Suggest a general way to deal with the magnesium nitride.

_____

_____

To deal with the magnesium nitride, you will add water. This step will convert the magnesium nitride to magnesium hydroxide and ammonia gas (NH_3).

5. Write the balanced equation for the reaction between magnesium nitride and water.

_____

There is still a problem though! Instead of a mixture of magnesium oxide and magnesium nitride, we now have a mixture of magnesium hydroxide and magnesium oxide. But there's a very easy way to fix this. If we heat magnesium hydroxide, it decomposes into solid magnesium oxide and water vapor.

6. Write the balanced equation for the decomposition of magnesium hydroxide.

_____

K Now let's do what you just wrote about. ***Make sure that your crucible is cool enough to touch.*** Using the transfer pipette, add 10 drops of water uniformly over the crucible's contents.

MAGNESIUM FIRES

Magnesium is extremely flammable! And magnesium fires can't be put out with water or even with carbon dioxide fire extinguishers—both of these substances make magnesium fires worse. They are usually put out with dry sand or other special fire extinguishers designed to extinguish metal fires.

Do not add water to a hot crucible!

7. Do you detect any recognizable odor? If so, describe the odor. Can you identify the substance?

_____

_____

L Carefully heat the crucible without its cover until the water evaporates; then heat strongly for several minutes.

M Allow the crucible, cover, and contents to cool to room temperature. Measure their combined mass and record your data in Table 1.

N Calculate the mass of the magnesium oxide and record your answer in Table 1.

O Finally, calculate the mass of the oxygen that chemically combined with the magnesium to form magnesium oxide. Record your answer in Table 1.

Analysis

8. Use your starting mass of magnesium and your mass of oxygen to calculate the moles of each.

9. Divide both mole values by the smaller value to get the ratio in whole numbers.

10. Determine the empirical formula for magnesium oxide. Was it what you predicted in Question 3?

_____

11. Using the masses of magnesium and magnesium oxide obtained during the experiment, calculate the observed (experimental) percent composition of magnesium in your magnesium oxide.

12. Calculate the actual percent composition of magnesium in magnesium oxide from the formula MgO by assuming a 1 mol sample (see Example 11-6 on page 247 of your textbook).

13. Calculate your percent error.

14. How does this experiment demonstrate the law of definite composition?

_____

_____

_____

TABLE 1

	Mass (g)
Crucible and Cover	
Crucible, Cover, and Magnesium	
Magnesium	
Crucible, Cover, and Magnesium Oxide—First Mass	
Magnesium Oxide Produced	
Oxygen	

11B LAB

Chymestry

Using Stoichiometric Relationships

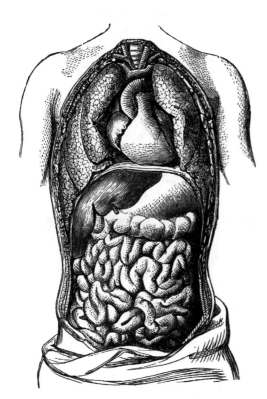

W hen food particles enter your stomach, they encounter gastric acids and enzymes that turn them into a slurry called *chyme*. Gastric acids are fairly strong, with a pH of 1–2, and they are mostly hydrochloric acid (HCl). At the beginning of your small intestine, your pancreas injects some sodium hydrogen carbonate (NaHCO$_3$) into the mixture. This neutralizes the acids so that they don't irritate the rest of your digestive system.

In this lab activity, you are going to re-create the contents of your small intestine! You will be reacting HCl with sodium hydrogen carbonate to see what happens. The goal is for you to measure the mole ratios of the reactants and the products so that you can figure out the stoichiometric relationships in the balanced chemical reaction of these two substances. You will measure the masses of both products and reactants to help you determine the mole ratios of each.

What chemistry takes place in my small intestine?

© 2021 BJU Press. Reproduction prohibited.

Procedure

1. Write the chemical reaction of NaHCO$_3$ with HCl and predict what you think the products will be.

_____

SETTING UP

A Clean an evaporating dish and rinse it with water from a wash bottle.

B Using the crucible tongs, hold the evaporating dish in a well-adjusted burner flame for several minutes to remove all the moisture.

QUESTION

» How are the moles of reactants and products related in a chemical reaction?

EQUIPMENT

- laboratory burner and lighter
- laboratory balance
- evaporating dish
- wash bottle
- crucible tongs
- spatula
- small watch glass
- test tube
- test tube rack
- transfer pipette
- wire gauze
- ring stand and ring
- sodium hydrogen carbonate (NaHCO$_3$)
- hydrochloric acid (HCl), 6 M
- goggles
- laboratory apron
- nitrile gloves

C After the dish is cool, measure its mass. Record your data in Table 1.

2. Why is it important for the evaporating dish to be cool and dry?

_____

_____

_____

_____

D Using the spatula, add about 3 g of the $NaHCO_3$ to the evaporating dish while it is still on the balance. Record the combined mass of the dish and $NaHCO_3$ in Table 1.

E Calculate the mass of sodium hydrogen carbonate and record it in Table 1.

REACTING NaHCO₃ WITH HCl

F Cover the evaporating dish with a small watch glass to keep chemicals from splattering during the reaction.

This is how you *slowly* add acid with a pipette.

G Pour about 6 mL of 6 M HCl into a clean test tube. Gradually add the acid to the $NaHCO_3$ with a transfer pipette or dropper. Allow the drops to enter the lip of the evaporating dish so that they flow down the side *gradually and slowly* (see left).

H Continue adding the acid drop by drop until the reaction stops and there is no more fizzing. Do not add more acid than is necessary. Tilt the dish from side to side to make sure that the acid has reached all the solid.

3. What substance do you think is producing the fizzing that you are observing?

_____

There are actually two reactions going on here. In the first reaction, the hydrochloric acid reacts with the sodium hydrogen carbonate to produce sodium chloride and carbonic acid. In the second reaction, the carbonic acid decomposes to form carbon dioxide gas and water.

4. Does this description of the reactions support your conclusion in Question 3? Explain.

_____

_____

What you have left in your evaporating dish is a mix of salt and water.

I Remove the watch glass and, using a wash bottle, rinse any splattered material from the underside of the watch glass with a small amount of distilled water. Be careful to wash all the material into the evaporating dish so that no NaCl is lost (see left).

5. Write the balanced equation for the reaction between sodium bicarbonate and hydrochloric acid to produce sodium chloride and carbonic acid.

_____

6. Write the balanced equation for the decomposition of carbonic acid.

_____

7. Now add these two equations together, canceling out any products from the first reaction that were consumed in the second reaction.

8. What do you predict will be the stoichiometric ratio of sodium hydrogen carbonate to sodium chloride? How do you know? Record your prediction in Table 2.

_____

_____

FINDING THE MASS OF NaCl

Let's see whether your answer to Question 8 is right.

J   Place the evaporating dish, supported by the wire gauze, on the ring stand. Heat the water in the evaporating dish until it boils gently. Do not let the water boil over or you will lose some of the NaCl and spoil the experiment.

K   Continue to heat the dish until most of the water has evaporated. Continue heating gently until the NaCl is dry.

L   Turn off the burner and allow the dish to cool; then weigh it and record its mass in Table 1.

M   Calculate the mass of NaCl produced and record your answer in Table 1.

Analysis

9. Calculate the number of moles of $NaHCO_3$ used and the number of moles of NaCl produced in the reaction. Show your work below and record your answers in Table 2.

10. Divide both mole amounts of $NaHCO_3$ and NaCl by the smaller of the two to give your experimental ratio between $NaHCO_3$ and NaCl. Record the mole ratio of $NaHCO_3$ to NaCl in Table 2.

11. How did this ratio compare to what you predicted in Question 8?

_____

12. So what did you use to determine the stoichiometric ratios between $NaHCO_3$ and NaCl?

_____

Going Further

13. Now that you've seen how sodium hydrogen carbonate reacts with hydrochloric acid, explain how eating too much acidic foodstuffs can cause heartburn.

   _____

   _____

   _____

   _____

14. What is the usual treatment for heartburn? What makes that treatment effective?

   _____

   _____

   _____

   _____

TABLE 1 *Data*

	Mass (g)
Evaporating Dish	
Evaporating Dish and NaHCO$_3$	
NaHCO$_3$	
Evaporating Dish and NaCl	
NaCl	

TABLE 2 *Results*

Predicted Ratio $n_{NaHCO_3} : n_{NaCl}$	
Moles NaHCO$_3$	
Moles NaCl	
Experimental Ratio $n_{NaHCO_3} : n_{NaCl}$	

Name _____

Date _____

Cold and Calculating

Finding Absolute Zero

Some people live in locations with extremely low temperatures. For example, in Dudinka, Russia, the average low temperature in January is −33 °C (240 K). How close is this to the coldest possible temperature?

In 1665 Robert Boyle suggested that there was a limit to how cold temperatures could go—a *primum frigidum*. Today we know this temperature as *absolute zero*. For centuries people theorized about the existence of absolute zero and made guesses about its value on various temperature scales. In 1848 Lord Kelvin devised his temperature scale, placing absolute zero at the lowest end. Since then scientists have tried to get measured temperatures as close as possible to absolute zero. They theorize that there could be temperatures in space that are smaller than a quadrillionth of a kelvin.

This lab activity recreates a historical experiment in an attempt to find absolute zero.

How can we determine an impossibly cold temperature?

QUESTIONS

» How does changing temperature affect the volume of a sample of gas?

» How can I model the relationship between the volume and temperature of a gas?

» How do scientists know what temperature is absolute zero?

EQUIPMENT

- laboratory burner and lighter
- watch glass
- crucible tongs
- laboratory thermometer
- beaker, 1000 mL
- glass stirring rod
- metric ruler
- melting point capillary tubes (2)
- masking tape
- vegetable oil
- ice cubes
- goggles
- laboratory apron
- nitrile gloves

Procedure

A Pour about 10 drops of vegetable oil onto the watch glass. Light the laboratory burner.

B Using tongs, carefully hold one of the capillary tubes with the open end slanted upward. Pass the entire length of the tube through the burner flame several times. Immediately dip the open end of the heated tube into the oil on the watch glass and allow it to cool and draw up a "plug" of oil about 1 cm long. You may need to hold the tube in the oil for a second or two to draw up the oil. When cooled to room temperature, the length of the column of air trapped in the tube should be about 5–7 cm.

C Repeat Step B with the second capillary tube.

1. What is the purpose of the oil plug?

_____

_____

2. Describe the temperature, pressure, and volume conditions inside the trapped air in the capillary tube.

_____

_____

_____

_____

D Attach the capillary tubes containing trapped air—with their open ends upward—to the thermometer using small pieces of tape, as shown at left.

3. Which gas law applies to these conditions? Explain.

_____

_____

_____

_____

E Fill the beaker about two-thirds full of water and ice. Hold the thermometer in the water close to the beaker wall so that you can read the temperature scale and see the location of the oil plugs in the capillary tubes. The entire air columns of both tubes must be submerged, but their open ends must stay above the water line.

If you allow the tube to get too hot, the length of trapped air column will be too small, resulting in larger relative errors. On the other hand, if you do not heat the capillary tube enough, the air column will be too long, making it impossible for you to obtain data at higher temperatures.

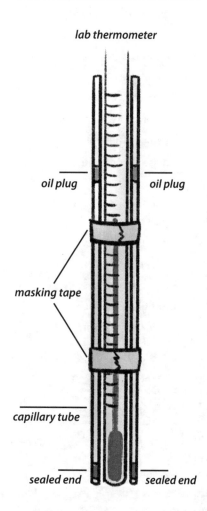

lab thermometer

oil plug   *oil plug*

masking tape

capillary tube

sealed end   *sealed end*

This is the setup that you will use to determine the value of absolute zero.

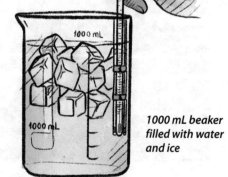

1000 mL beaker filled with water and ice

GETTING NUMBERS

F Allow the temperature to stabilize. Stirring the bath periodically with a stirring rod will speed up this process.

4. Why do you think that stirring the ice water promotes temperature stabilization?

_____

_____

_____

5. Predict the temperature for the air column after it stabilizes in the ice-water bath.

_____

G Once the temperature has stabilized, measure and record the temperature in Table 1.

H Wait an additional minute. Carefully place the ruler in the water next to one of the capillary tubes. Measure the height of the air column, from the top of the melted glass to the bottom of the oil plug. Do *not* include either the melted glass itself or the oil plug in the measurement. Record your data in Table 1. Repeat for the other capillary tube.

6. What are some possible sources of error in your measurements of the air columns?

_____

_____

I Repeat Steps E–H with cold tap water (approximately 20 °C), warm tap water (approximately 35 °C), and hot tap water (approximately 50 °C). If you can't get sufficiently hot water from the tap for the fourth data point, use a hot plate or laboratory burner to heat the water. Do not exceed 50 °C.

Analysis

DETERMINING ABSOLUTE ZERO

J Using a graphing calculator or spreadsheet program, create scatterplots of the height values (*y*-axis) and temperatures (*x*-axis) for each tube.

7. What relationship do you think would fit the graphs?

_____

K Draw a curve of best fit for each set of data points.

8. Determine the equation for the best-fit curves that you drew for Step K.

_____

MEASURING THE AIR COLUMN

In this cold-water bath, you will probably need to wipe off the condensation from the beaker to get a clear view of the capillary tubes. Be careful that you do not knock the beaker off the wire gauze and ring when making your measurements! Put the ruler into the water with the capillary tubes to measure the height of your column. When you measure the height of your air column, be sure not to include the oil plug.

9. Use the equations that you determined in Question 8 to calculate the temperature (absolute zero) at which the height would be zero. Average the two values for your final answer.

_____

10. Calculate the percent error for your value, using −273 °C as the theoretical, or actual value, of absolute zero.

_____

Going Further

11. To calculate absolute zero, you assume that the height of the air column is zero. Is this condition realistic? What could this imply?

_____

_____

_____

_____

_____

TABLE 1

Temperature (*t*) in °C	Length (*h*) in cm	
	Tube 1	Tube 2

© 2021 BJU Press. Reproduction prohibited.

EQUIPMENT

- barometer
- laboratory balance
- graduated cylinder, 25 mL
- large test tube
- test tube rack
- spatula
- Erlenmeyer flask, 500 mL
- pinchcock clamp
- glass and rubber tubing
- rubber stoppers, 1-hole and 2-hole
- beaker, 600 mL
- graduated cylinder, 100 mL
- laboratory thermometer
- weighing paper
- 3.00% hydrogen peroxide (H_2O_2), 15.0 mL
- manganese(IV) oxide (MnO_2), 1 g
- goggles
- laboratory apron
- nitrile gloves

An Aquanaut's World

Predicting the Production of Oxygen

About sixty feet down on the sandy floor of the Florida Keys by a coral reef rests a yellow metal structure. It isn't a sunken ship or a submarine—it's an underwater laboratory.

Aquarius is one of the few underwater laboratories on Earth dedicated to scientific pursuits. The scientists who work there—called *aquanauts*—live at higher pressures, spending long amounts of time exploring the ocean floor. They don't decompress until their mission is done.

How can we predict the volume of gas produced in a reaction?

Air is supplied to the laboratory by a surface buoy that houses a compressor. The divers use and recharge their air tanks during missions to explore for up to eight hours. A room in Aquarius maintains pressure to match that of the ocean so that a moon pool can be used to easily enter the marine environment. Life and work at Aquarius is all about two things that you'll explore in this lab activity—pressure and oxygen.

In this experiment, you will predict the mass of oxygen gas generated in a reaction. Then you will compare this experimental value to a theoretical value to determine your percent error.

QUESTIONS

» How do I collect a sample of gas over water?

» How can I determine the amount of a dry gas that was produced over water?

Procedure

A. Determine today's atmospheric pressure and record your data in Table 1.

B. In the 25 mL graduated cylinder, measure out exactly 15.0 mL of hydrogen peroxide (H_2O_2). Record this volume in Table 1. Pour the H_2O_2 into the test tube, which we will refer to as the *reaction tube*.

C. Given that the density of 3.00% hydrogen peroxide solution is 1.01 g/mL at room temperature, determine the mass of the H_2O_2 solution. Show your work below and record your answer in Table 1.

D. Determine the mass of the H_2O_2 (solute) in the solution. Show your work below and record your answer in Table 1.

E On a piece of weighing paper, use a spatula to obtain and measure out about 1 g of manganese(IV) oxide. The exact amount is not critical. *Do not put it into the reaction tube yet.*

1. The manganese(IV) oxide isn't actually going to react with the hydrogen peroxide. It is speeding up the reaction in which H_2O_2 releases oxygen. What kind of substance is MnO_2 in this reaction?

_____

_____

2. In this reaction, you will be using hydrogen peroxide in the presence of manganese(IV) oxide to produce oxygen gas and water. Write the balanced chemical equation for this reaction, showing where all these chemicals and conditions fit in.

_____

3. What kind of chemical reaction is this?

_____

4. Now predict the volume of oxygen gas that will be produced at STP. Record your answer in Table 1.

F Assemble the rest of the setup as shown below. Fill the 500 mL Erlenmeyer flask with water to just below the neck. Make sure that the bottom end of the reaction side glass tube is about 0.5 cm below the rubber stopper. Check to see that the water exit side glass tube is 0.5 cm above the bottom of the flask. Keep the water exit tubing clamped with the pinchcock to keep water from running out. Wet the rubber stopper before you insert it in the flask's mouth to improve the seal.

G Ask your teacher to check your setup.

NO PROJECTILES!

Point the reaction tube away from people while observing the reaction as much as possible, just in case the rubber stopper comes loose. We don't want any projectiles!

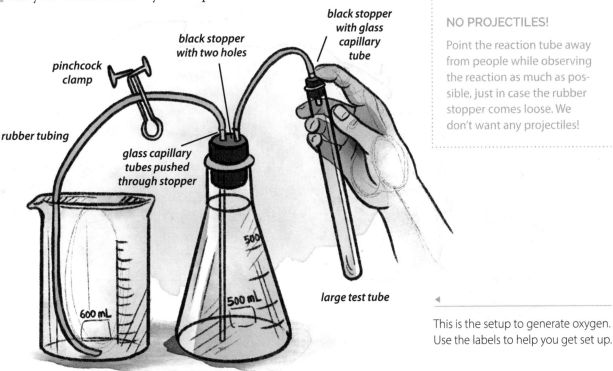

pinchcock clamp

black stopper with two holes

black stopper with glass capillary tube

rubber tubing

glass capillary tubes pushed through stopper

large test tube

600 mL beaker (empty)

500 mL flask (filled with water)

This is the setup to generate oxygen. Use the labels to help you get set up.

H Place about 100 mL of water in the beaker.

I Disconnect the reaction tube by removing the stopper with the tube attached. Remove the pinchcock clamp from the water exit tube.

J Tip the flask about 90° to the right so that water can flow through the water exit tube to produce a siphon (see below). The water will not siphon if there is a leak.

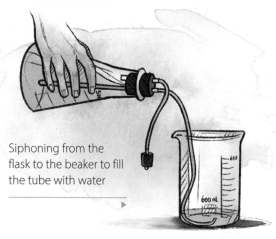

Siphoning from the flask to the beaker to fill the tube with water

K When the water exit tube has filled with water, set the flask down. At this point, water should continue siphoning from the flask into the beaker. Stop the siphoning by clamping the water exit tube with the clamp.

L Now siphon the water back into the flask so that the water level in the flask is just below the re-action side inlet tube. To do this, raise the beaker above the water level in the flask and remove the clamp (see below).

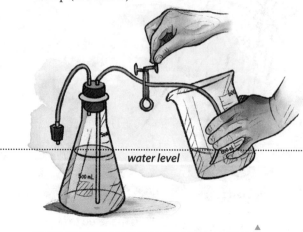

Siphon water from the beaker to the flask until the water level is just below the gas inlet tube.

M As soon as the flask fills to the desired level, replace the clamp and put the beaker back on the desk.

N Wet the reaction tube stopper and insert it into the mouth of the test tube. Confirm that both stoppers are snug.

O Remove the clamp. The water level in the flask will fall slightly. After this change, the water level should remain at the new position.

P Equalize the air pressure in the flask with that of the atmosphere by lifting the beaker so that its water level is even with the water level in the flask. Replace the clamp while the water levels are matched (see below). Once you've clamped the tube, you can put the beaker back on the table.

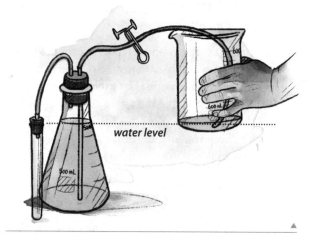

Equalize the pressure in your tubes by lining up the water levels in the Erlenmeyer flask and the beaker. Put on the pinchcock clamp when water levels are equal.

5. Why is it important that there are no leaks or bubbles in your setup and that the air pressure in the flask be equal to atmospheric pressure?

_____

_____

_____

_____

_____

Q Empty and dry the beaker and return it to the assembly.

MAKING OXYGEN

R Remove the stopper from the reaction tube and pour the manganese(IV) oxide into the hydrogen peroxide solution. Quickly replace the stopper and remove the clamp. Hold the reaction tube vertically near the top. With one finger, hold the stopper firmly in place. Swirl the tube to speed up the reaction. Every few seconds, give the tube another swirl.

6. Record anything that you observe during the reaction, including changes in the reaction mixture, the space of air over the water in the flask, and the amount of water in the beaker.

_____

_____

_____

7. Are the reaction conditions for your production of oxygen gas STP conditions? Explain.

_____

_____

_____

S After about 10 minutes, very little water should be coming out of the water exit tube. Consider the reaction finished at this point even though the mixture in the reaction tube may still be bubbling slightly.

8. The volume of water in the beaker represents the volume of displaced water. What else does this volume equal?

_____

T Lift the beaker so that its water level matches the water level in the flask. Clamp the water exit tube with the clamp. Immediately remove the stopper from the reaction tube so that it doesn't pop out under pressure!

U Using the 100 mL graduated cylinder, determine the volume of the water displaced by the oxygen produced and record the result in Table 1.

V Measure the temperature of the water in the graduated cylinder. Convert the result to kelvins and record this temperature in Table 1.

W Determine the water vapor pressure at the temperature measured in Step V. Record this value in Table 1.

9. Why do you need to take the temperature of the water?

_____

_____

_____

10. Look back at Question 2. Where did the oxygen, water, and manganese(IV) oxide go after the hydrogen peroxide began to react?

_____

_____

_____

11. Use Dalton's law to determine the partial pressure of oxygen. Show your work below and record your answer in Table 1.

12. Now use gas laws to find the volume of the oxygen if the conditions were changed to STP. Show your work below and record your answer in Table 1.

13. Look back at your predicted value for the volume of oxygen gas generated at STP from the decomposition of H_2O_2. Do a yield calculation for this experiment. Show your work below and record your answer in Table 1.

14. Explain possible causes for quantities of oxygen smaller or larger than predicted.

   _____

   _____

   _____

   _____

   _____

   _____

   _____

   _____

   _____

Going Further

15. Not only was your experiment today *not* at STP, the aquanaut's world isn't at STP either! In fact, if these research scientists don't consider the pressure and temperature conditions, it could cost them their lives. How do you think aquanauts need to adjust for these conditions?

   _____

   _____

   _____

   _____

   _____

16. Can you think of another career in which changes to pressures and temperatures of gases must be considered?

_____

_____

_____

_____

_____

TABLE 1

Atmospheric Pressure (kPa)	
Volume H_2O_2 Solution (mL)	
Mass of H_2O_2 Solution (g)	
Mass of H_2O_2 (g)	
Predicted Volume Oxygen (L)	
Measured Volume Oxygen (L)	
Temperature (K)	
Water Vapor Pressure (kPa)	
Pressure of Oxygen (kPa)	
Volume Oxygen at STP (L)	
Percent Yield	

EQUIPMENT

- computer with internet access
- magnifying glass
- stereomicroscope
- minerals

Cracking the Crystal

Relating Geology to Chemistry

Along the shores of an acid lake in Indonesia, miners eke out a living by gathering sulfur from naturally occurring deposits, despite the risk of breathing air laced with toxic sulfuric acid. The miners sell the sulfur, some of it later carved into statues and figures.

The sulfur that these miners gather grows in characteristic crystals. You've spent some time in your textbook learning how crystal shapes affect the formation of minerals. Now you get an opportunity to explore minerals on your own, looking at some real minerals and thinking about what is happening at the atomic level to produce the crystals that you hold in your hand.

Your goal for this activity is to explain the crystal shapes of different minerals using their chemical crystal structures.

What determines the shape of a crystal?

QUESTIONS

» What distinguishes one type of crystal from another?

» How is the shape of a crystal related to its molecular or ionic structure?

Procedure

A Make sure that you are thinking about minerals and not rocks. Minerals are more often chemically pure substances.

B Think about the kind of chemical that you are dealing with: an atomic crystal, a covalent molecular crystal, a covalent network crystal, an ionic crystal, or a metallic crystal.

C Try to determine the formula for the crystal that you are examining. Sketch it out, identifying the atoms in your formula unit somehow.

D Some minerals may be allotropes. Watch out for these!

E Try to get an actual sample. If you can't, harness the power of the internet to look at lots of different pictures of your mineral.

F If you have a sample, examine it with a magnifying glass or a stereo-microscope. If you are working with digital pictures of minerals, zoom in to see lots of detail.

G In Table 1, record your observations or notes on the minerals that you examine.

THINK ABOUT IT

1. Sulfur is an example of an atomic crystal that has many allotropes. In its solid state, it can appear in granular deposits or as an orthorhombic crystal. The number of sulfur atoms that form rings in the formula unit of these crystals can range from six to as many as twenty. Why do you think sulfur forms such a wide range of crystals?

_____

_____

2. What do you think determines the form that sulfur will take?

_____

_____

Sulfur crystals (yellow) in aragonite

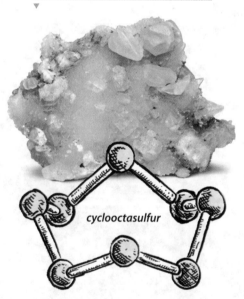

cyclooctasulfur

3. One of the most common forms of sulfur is cyclooctasulfur, S_8. In nature, it forms crystals with a rhombohedral shape. Using the photograph shown at left, write a paragraph that relates the shape of the formula unit to its crystal shape.

_____

_____

_____

_____

_____

4. The opener to this lab activity shows how people are mining sulfur from a lake in Indonesia. Why is it important to investigate crystals like sulfur and their properties?

_____

_____

_____

TABLE 1

Mineral	Observations	Sketches

13B LAB

Forces of Nature

Exploring Intermolecular Forces in Liquids

Many ponds across North America freeze over in winter. Yet in many of those ponds, safe within their icebound lodges, beavers carry on with daily activities. When not lounging in their lodges, they can exit through underwater doors to swim beneath the ice.

Why does ice form on the surface of ponds? If water behaved like most liquids, ice would be denser than liquid water, making it sink to the bottom of the pond. The intermolecular forces in water—London dispersion forces, dipole-dipole forces, and, most of all, hydrogen bonds—make ice less dense than water, causing it to float. Because of this, beavers can survive under the ice.

What determines the physical properties of liquids?

In this lab activity, you will investigate the intermolecular forces in four liquids—water, acetone (CH_3COCH_3), ethanol (CH_3CH_2OH), and mineral oil. The four liquids have different properties because they are made of molecules containing different arrangements of atoms. Let's see how intermolecular forces affect a liquid's density, viscosity, surface tension, solubility, and ease of evaporation.

QUESTIONS

» How do the viscosity, surface tension, solubility, and volatility of different liquids compare?

» How are the physical properties of liquids related to the polarity of their molecules?

» How are the physical properties of liquids related to the molecular masses of their molecules?

» Can we explain how intermolecular forces affect the characteristics of liquids on the basis of empirical data?

EQUIPMENT

- **probeware with temperature probe**
- **prepared test tubes with marbles (4)**
- **stopwatch**
- **beakers, 100 mL (5)**
- **marker or labeling tape**
- **watch glass**
- **pipettes (4)**
- **small test tubes (3)**
- **food coloring**
- **water (20 mL)**
- **acetone (20 mL)**
- **ethanol (20 mL)**
- **mineral oil (20 mL)**
- **pennies (4)**
- **food coloring**
- **filter paper**
- **goggles**
- **laboratory apron**
- **nitrile gloves**

Procedure

Before you get started, let's think about the substances that you will be working with. Notice their Lewis structures below. Mineral oil is represented by pentadecane, a 15-carbon molecule.

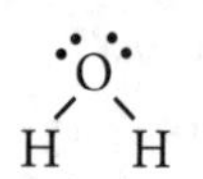

water 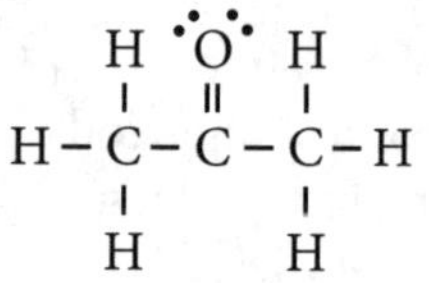   *acetone* 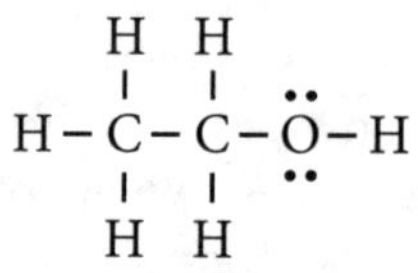   *ethanol*

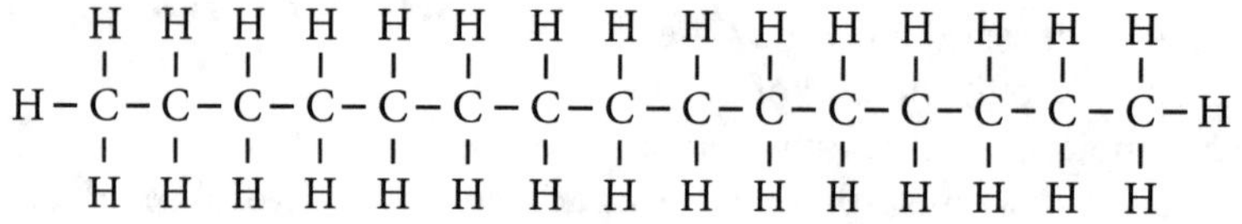

pentadecane

1. Which of the four substances are polar?

_____

Dipole Moment Data

water: 1.85 D

acetone: 2.91 D

ethanol: 1.69 D

pentadecane: 0 D

An *electric dipole moment*—a measure of polarity—can be measured for a molecule and assigned a number. While the SI unit for electric dipole moment is the *coulomb meter*, a unit called the *debye (D)* is more commonly used. The debye is the measure of charge and the distance that separates areas of charge. The dipole moments for pure samples of the four liquids are provided in the box shown at left.

2. Using the dipole moment measurements in the box, which substance do you think is the most polar?

_____

3. Which molecule has the highest molecular mass? Which one has the lowest?

_____

4. How do you think the mass of the molecule will affect the way that it responds to intermolecular forces?

_____

_____

_____

Think for a moment about the polarity and molecular weight of acetone. Throughout this lab activity, you will make some predictions about how acetone's physical properties will compare with those of the other three liquids. Then you'll explore how intermolecular forces affect the manner in which these liquids behave.

VISCOSITY

Viscosity, a liquid's resistance to flow, is measured in Pa·s, or pascal-seconds. The pascal is a unit of pressure, and pascal-seconds are related to the rate of flow of a liquid. The higher its viscosity value, the thicker and more resistant to flow a liquid will be. Viscosity is a form of cohesion.

5. With 4 being the highest and 1 being the lowest, predict acetone's viscosity compared with the other three liquids.

_____

A Notice that there is a marble at the bottom of each of the four large, labeled, stoppered test tubes. Swirl the contents of each test tube.

6. Which liquid do you think is the most viscous?

_____

B Now let's find out whether you're right. Give the stopwatch to one person designated from your group to be the timer.

C One at a time, invert each tube so that the marble settles to the stoppered end of the test tube.

D Invert each tube again, starting the stopwatch as soon as the test tube is in the upright position. Stop the stopwatch as soon as the marble reaches the bottom of the test tube. Record the time in Table 1.

E Repeat Steps D and E to complete three trials for each labeled test tube.

F Average your trials to find one value for the time of the marble's fall for each liquid.

7. Why should you do more than one trial for each liquid?

_____

_____

8. In which liquid did the marble take the longest to fall? How does this relate to viscosity? Did this follow your prediction?

_____

_____

_____

9. Explain why you think this liquid was the most viscous.

_____

_____

_____

10. How do intermolecular forces affect viscosity?

_____

_____

_____

Consider the viscosities of pure samples of the four liquids at room temperature provided in the box shown at left.

Viscosity Data

water: 1.002 mPa·s

acetone: 0.3311 mPa·s

ethanol: 1.114 mPa·s

pentadecane: 2.863 mPa·s

11. How do these values of viscosity relate to what you observed?

____

____

12. Evaluate your prediction of acetone's viscosity.

____

____

____

SURFACE TENSION

13. With 4 being the highest and 1 being the lowest, predict acetone's surface tension compared with the other three liquids.

____

G Fill four 100 mL beakers with fresh samples of each of the four liquids; label each one.

H Wash four pennies with detergent, then dry. Put a large watch glass on top of your laboratory bench and put a paper towel on it. Place the four pennies on the paper towel. Label the paper towel to show which liquid will be placed atop each penny.

14. How is the surface tension of a liquid related to the number of drops of that liquid that you could fit on a penny?

____

____

____

I Using a clean pipette, add the first liquid to its penny one drop at a time until the liquid overflows onto the paper towel. Keep a careful count of the drops and record them in Table 2. Do this step as quickly as possible since some of the liquids evaporate fairly rapidly. Repeat for the other three liquids.

J Clean all four pennies well, then dry. Repeat Step I a second time for all four liquids, and record your results in Table 2.

K Average your results and record this data in Table 2.

15. Which liquid has the highest surface tension? Why do you think this is so?

_____

_____

_____

_____

16. How do intermolecular forces affect surface tension?

_____

_____

_____

_____

17. Evaluate your prediction of acetone's surface tension.

_____

_____

_____

_____

_____

SOLUBILITY

18. Do you think acetone will mix with water?

_____

L Fill three small test tubes halfway, one with acetone, another with ethanol, and the last with mineral oil. Label your test tubes.

M Fill a 100 mL beaker three-quarters full with water. Add a few drops of food coloring.

N Add the colored water to the three test tubes until they are almost full.

19. What do you observe about the three liquids?

_____

_____

20. Explain why your liquids behaved the way that they did on the basis of intermolecular forces. (*Hint*: See page 315 of your textbook.)

_____

_____

_____

_____

_____

When two liquids mix together or one dissolves in the other, they are said to be *miscible*.

21. How do intermolecular forces relate to miscibility?

_____

_____

_____

22. Evaluate your prediction of acetone's ability to dissolve in water.

_____

_____

_____

_____

VOLATILITY

The ease at which a liquid evaporates into a gas is called its *volatility*.

23. With 4 being the highest and 1 being the lowest, predict acetone's volatility compared with the other four liquids.

_____

O   Plug in the temperature probe for your probeware.

P   Wrap a single layer of filter paper around the end of the temperature probe and secure it with tape. Trim or tear off any excess.

Q   Dip the tip covered in filter paper in one of the four liquids until the paper is saturated. Take the probe out of the beaker, touching the probe to the inside of the beaker to eliminate any drips.

R   Tape the probe onto the edge of the laboratory bench as shown at left. Press the probeware's **Collect** button or equivalent. If your probeware displays real-time data, watch how the temperature changes over time.

TESTING YOUR LIQUIDS

If you have any liquid left in the 100 mL beakers from the surface tension test, you may use that, or you can get about 5 mL of liquid in the same beakers.

Setup for testing the volatility of your liquids

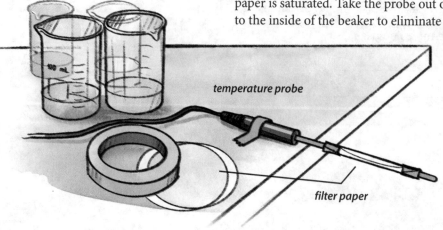

temperature probe

filter paper

S Collect data for three minutes. Follow the instructions for your probe-ware to analyze the data and calculate statistical trends.

T Locate the maximum and minimum temperature values and subtract the maximum value from the minimum. The result represents the temperature change caused by the evaporating liquid. Record this value in the appropriate row of Table 3.

U Remove the filter paper and wipe the probe with a paper towel.

Repeat steps P through U for the other three liquids and record the temperature changes in Table 3. Make sure that you change the filter paper each time!

24. Why did the temperature drop noticeably for some samples over time?

_____

_____

25. According to your data, which liquid did you observe to evaporate the most quickly? How do you know?

_____

_____

_____

26. Check the boiling point data of the four liquids provided in the box shown at right. How does what you observed relate to their boiling points?

_____

_____

_____

Boiling Point Data
water: 100 °C
acetone: 56–57 °C
ethanol: 78.5 °C
pentadecane: 212.41 °C

27. How do intermolecular forces affect volatility?

_____

_____

28. Evaluate your prediction of acetone's volatility.

_____

_____

_____

29. Look back at the Lewis structures of the four liquids. What properties of these molecules affected their viscosity, surface tension, solubility, and volatility?

_____

_____

_____

_____

On the basis of the data that you have been given in this lab activity and the experimentation that you have done, you will now rank the properties of the four liquids. Record your results in Table 4.

V Rank the polarity of all four liquids, with 4 being the highest and 1 being the lowest.

W Rank the molecular weight of all four liquids, with 1 being the highest and 4 being the lowest. This scale has been reversed because molecular weight and the influence of intermolecular forces are inversely related.

X Rank the viscosity of all four liquids, with 1 representing the most resistance to flow and 4 the lowest resistance to flow.

Y Rank the surface tension of all four liquids, with 4 being the highest and 1 being the lowest.

Z Assign water a miscibility score of 4. For the other liquids, if the liquid is miscible in water, assign a score of 4. If it is not, assign a score of 0.

AA Rank the volatility of all four liquids, with 1 being the least volatile (having the highest boiling point) and 4 being the most volatile (having the lowest boiling point).

BB Add up your scores.

30. What kind of scores do the polar molecules have? How does this compare with nonpolar molecules?

_____

_____

_____

31. How do these scores relate to what you observed about water and acetone?

_____

_____

_____

32. How do these scores relate to how ethanol compares with water and acetone?

_____

_____

_____

33. How do these scores relate to what you observed about mineral oil?

_____

_____

_____

34. Relate all these comparisons to the types of intermolecular forces that these liquids experience.

_____

_____

_____

_____

TABLE 1 *Time of the Marble's Fall (s)*

	Trial 1	**Trial 2**	**Trial 3**	**Average**
In Water				
In Acetone				
In Ethanol				
In Mineral Oil				

TABLE 2 *Number of Drops*

	# of Drops to Cover a Penny		**Average # of Drops to Cover a Penny**
	Trial 1	**Trial 2**	
Water			
Acetone			
Ethanol			
Mineral Oil			

TABLE 3 *Temperature Change during Evaporation*

	Change (°C)
Water	
Acetone	
Ethanol	
Mineral Oil	

TABLE 4 *Ranking the Four Liquids on the Basis of Experimentation*

	Water	Acetone	Ethanol	Mineral Oil
Polarity				
Molecular Weight				
Viscosity				
Surface Tension				
Miscibility				
Volatility				
Sum of Scores				

EQUIPMENT

- hot plate
- laboratory balance
- beaker, 250 mL
- medium-sized test tubes (4)
- test tube rack
- spatula
- weighing paper
- graduated cylinder, 10 mL
- glass stirring rod
- test tube clamp
- laboratory thermometer
- masking tape or grease pencil
- ammonium chloride (NH_4Cl), 21.00 g
- distilled water
- goggles
- laboratory apron
- nitrile gloves

One Giant Solution

Making a Solubility Curve

Y ou've learned that solubility is the amount of solute that will dissolve in a given amount of solvent to make a saturated solution. Think of the ocean as one giant solution! And in that solution, the fish and the plankton and algae they feed on need dissolved oxygen. Colder waters are able to hold more oxygen since the solubility of gases increases with decreasing temperature. So the solubility of ocean water varies with different conditions such as temperature. You will get to see this for yourself in this lab activity as you vary the temperature of a solution and observe how solids dissolved in the solution respond to those changes.

How does temperature affect the solubility of a salt?

QUESTIONS

» How does changing the temperature of a solvent alter the solubility of a salt?

» How do scientists make a solubility curve?

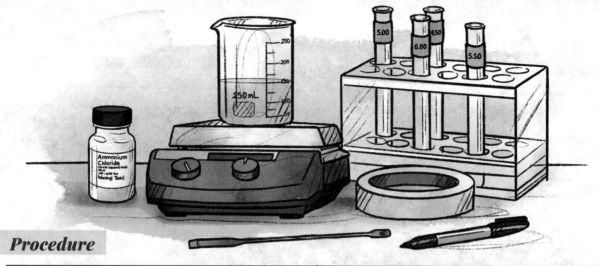

Procedure

A Add about 150 mL of water to the beaker. Check the water level by immersing the four test tubes in the water. Water level should be near the top of the beaker. Move the test tubes back to the test tube rack.

B Place the beaker on the hot plate and set the hot plate on medium-high. Adjust the temperature of the hot plate to keep the hot water bath near boiling.

C Label the test tubes as follows: "6.00," "5.50," "5.00," and "4.50."

D Using the spatula, weighing paper, and laboratory balance, measure approximately 6.00 g of ammonium chloride and record the exact mass in Table 1. Add this to Tube 6.00.

E Repeat Step D with 5.50 g, 5.00 g, and 4.50 g of ammonium chloride in the appropriate test tubes.

1. Which sample will dissolve the quickest? Explain.

_____

_____

_____

F Using the graduated cylinder, add exactly 10.0 mL of distilled water to each test tube. You may want to use a pipette to control the addition of water.

2. Which test tube do you think will form crystals the quickest when cooled? Why?

_____

_____

_____

_____

G Place the four test tubes into the hot-water bath. Do not allow any water from the beaker to get into the test tubes!

3. Why is it important that no water from the hot-water bath get into the test tubes?

_____

_____

_____

_____

H Stir the solutions with the stirring rod to help dissolve the ammonium chloride. Be sure to rinse and dry the stirring rod before putting it into a different solution. When the solute in all four tubes has completely dissolved, turn off the hot plate.

4. Use the kinetic-molecular theory to describe why the hot-water bath speeds up the solvation process for solids.

_____

_____

_____

I Using the test tube clamp, remove Tube 6.00 from the water bath and place it in your test tube rack. Place a thermometer into the test tube and allow the solution to cool.

J When crystals start forming in the liquid, note the temperature and record it in Table 1. Double-check this temperature by reheating the test tube just enough to dissolve the solute again. If the temperatures for the first and second crystalli-zations differ by more than a few degrees, care-fully repeat the reheating and recooling process.

K Repeat Steps I and J for Tubes 5.50, 5.00, and 4.50.

5. Which tube formed crystals at the highest temperature? How did this compare with your prediction in Question 2?

_____

_____

_____

_____

CREATING A SOLUBILITY CURVE

L Create a scatterplot of the data from Table 1, including a curve of best fit that extends down to 0 °C and up to 100 °C.

6. Using your solubility curve, determine the solu-bility of ammonium chloride (in g/10.0 mL H_2O) at both 90 °C and 10 °C. Record your answers in Table 2.

7. Obtain the accepted values for the solubility of ammonium chloride at both 90 °C and 10 °C. Calculate your percent error. Record your an-swers in Table 2.

8. Describe how the shape of the solubility curve would change, if at all, if the actual temperatures were all 7 °C lower than what you measured.

_____

_____

_____

9. You have learned that the solubilities of gases decrease with increasing temperature. Predict how a solubility curve of a gas would look compared with one for a solid.

_____

_____

Going Further

10. In the introduction we noted that the ocean is one giant solution. The other solution that animals such as fish rely on is their blood. How are the solutions of ocean water and blood similar? How are they different?

_____

_____

_____

_____

_____

_____

TABLE 1 _Data_

Mass of NH_4Cl (g)	Temperature for Crystallization (°C)	
	Trial 1	**Trial 2**

TABLE 2 _Results_

Temperature (°C)	Solubility$_{measured}$ (g/10 mL)	Solubility$_{accepted}$ (g/10 mL)	Percent Error
90.0			
10.0			

Sugar, Sugar

Determining the Sugar Content in Beverages

Sports drinks, sweet tea, fruit juice, and soda are popular beverages. While these drinks come in many flavors, they all have one thing in common: they are all solutions, and their main ingredients are water and sugar.

How much sugar is really in my favorite beverage?

Have you ever read the nutrition label on these beverages? They all report the grams of sugar per serving. Do you think that the numbers reported are accurate? In this lab activity, you will measure how the density of a solution changes as more sugar is added to it. From this information, we will estimate the sugar in some common beverages. We will then compare this with the sugar content on the label.

QUESTIONS

» What is a calibration curve?

» How can I use density to determine the sugar content of a solution?

EQUIPMENT

- laboratory balance
- beakers, 50 mL (7)
- weighing boat
- stirring rod
- beaker, 100 mL
- volumetric pipette, 10 mL
- pipette bulb
- wash bottle with distilled water
- marker
- distilled water
- food coloring
- sugar
- beverages
- goggles
- laboratory apron

MAKING REFERENCE SOLUTIONS

A Label five of the 50 mL beakers as follows: "0," "5," "10," "15," and "20."

B Fill Beaker 0 with approximately 50 mL of distilled water.

C Using the laboratory balance, add 47.5 g of distilled water to Beaker 5. Add two drops of blue food coloring.

D Using the weighing boat and laboratory balance, measure out 2.50 g of table sugar. Add the sugar to Beaker 5 and stir until the sugar is dissolved.

E Repeat Steps C and D using Beaker 10, 45.0 g of distilled water, two drops of green food coloring, and 5.00 g of sugar.

F Repeat Steps C and D using Beaker 15, 42.5 g of water, two drops of yellow food coloring, and 7.50 g of sugar.

G Repeat Steps C and D using Beaker 20, 40.0 g of water, two drops of red food coloring, and 10.00 g of sugar.

H Measure the mass of the empty 100 mL beaker and record your data in Table 1.

I Using the volumetric pipette and bulb, transfer 10.00 mL of the clear reference solution (Beaker 0) into the 100 mL beaker.

J Measure the mass of the beaker and solution and record your data in Table 1.

K Repeat Steps H–J for the other four reference solutions. *Be sure to rinse the pipette with distilled water between each sample.*

1. Why is it important to rinse the pipette between each sample?

   _____

   _____

2. On the basis of your answer to Question 1, how could you modify the procedures to improve your results even more?

   _____

   _____

   _____

3. How can we find the masses and densities of the individual reference solutions when we don't empty the beaker between taking each mass?

   _____

   _____

   _____

4. Calculate the mass and density for each of the reference solutions. Record your answers in Table 1.

Hold the "A" valve and then squeeze the bulb to release air and create a vacuum. Press the "S" valve with the tip of the pipette in the solution to draw solution into the pipette. Release "S" when the liquid reaches the volumetric level. Use the "E" valve to release the liquid from the pipette.

CREATING A CALIBRATION CURVE

L. Create a scatterplot of the mass fraction (*x*-axis) and the density (*y*-axis) for the five reference solutions.

5. When plotting data such as that obtained in this experiment, why is it not appropriate to connect the dots?

_____

_____

_____

_____

6. Determine the equation of the line of best fit.

7. Does the *y*-intercept make sense? Explain.

_____

_____

_____

MEASURING THE BEVERAGES

M. Using your last two 50 mL beakers, obtain approximately 20 mL samples of two beverages. Record which beverages you chose in Table 2.

N. Refer to the nutritional label on the beverage and record the volume and grams of sugar. Record this data in Table 2.

O. Using the volumetric pipette and bulb, transfer 10.00 mL of the first beverage into the 100 mL beaker that is on the balance.

P. Measure the mass of the beaker and solution and record your data in Table 2.

Q. Rinse the pipette with distilled water.

R. Repeat Steps O–Q for the other beverage.

S Calculate the mass and density for each of the two beverages. Record your answers in Table 2.

8. Using the line of best fit from your scatterplot, estimate the mass fraction of the two beverages. Record your answers in Table 2.

9. Using your experimental density, experimental mass fraction, and the volume data from the nutrition label, determine the mass of sugar in each beverage.

10. Calculate the percent error for the grams of sugar for each beverage.

11. State a claim about the accuracy of the grams of sugar reported on the nutritional labels.

_____

_____

_____

_____

_____

Going Further

12. This lab activity looks at the relationship between the density of a beverage and its sugar content. How can you apply what you have learned in this lab activity to make appropriate choices in your sugar consumption? Explain.

_____

_____

_____

_____

_____

_____

_____

TABLE 1 *Reference Solutions*

Solution	Mass Fraction	V (mL)	Mass (g)	Solution Mass (g)	Density (g/mL)
Empty Beaker					
Clear	0.00%	10.00			
Blue	5.00%	10.00			
Green	10.0%	10.00			
Yellow	15.0%	10.00			
Red	20.0%	10.00			

TABLE 2 *Beverages*

Solution	Volume (mL)	Labeled Volume (mL)	Labeled Sugar Mass (g)	Beaker and Solution Mass (g)	Solution Mass (g)	Density (g/mL)	Experimental Mass Fraction	Experimental Sugar Mass (g)	Percent Error

15A LAB

Hot Shot

Finding the Specific Heat of a Metal

Have you ever absent-mindedly grabbed the handle of a cast iron skillet that's been sitting on a lit burner? Then you may have noticed how easily iron heats up! This is because of its low specific heat. In very simple terms, it doesn't take a lot of thermal energy to raise iron's temperature by 1 °C.

How can I measure how easily a material heats up?

In this lab activity, you will add some heated metal shot to water inside a simple calorimeter. You'll observe the thermal energy transfer to determine the specific heat of your metal.

QUESTIONS

» How can we observe energy transfer?

» How do I use the law of conservation of energy to account for thermal energy transfer?

» How can I determine the specific heat of a metal?

Procedure

SETTING UP

A Assemble a ring stand and ring, and place the wire gauze on the ring (see below).

B Fill a 250 mL beaker halfway with hot water and place it on the wire gauze, positioning your laboratory burner under the gauze. Light the laboratory burner and begin heating the water.

C While the water is heating, use the weighing dish and laboratory balance to obtain 50–70 g of metal shot. Measure the actual mass of the metal shot and transfer the shot to the test tube. Record the mass in Table 1.

EQUIPMENT

- laboratory burner and lighter
- laboratory balance
- ring stand and ring
- wire gauze
- beaker, 250 mL
- weighing dish
- medium test tube
- foam cups, 6–8 oz (2)
- graduated cylinder, 100 mL
- room-temperature distilled water
- thermometer
- beaker, 400 mL
- split rubber stopper, 1-hole, #4
- cardboard, 10 × 10 cm
- test tube clamp
- metal shot, 50–70 g
- goggles
- laboratory apron
- puncture-proof gloves

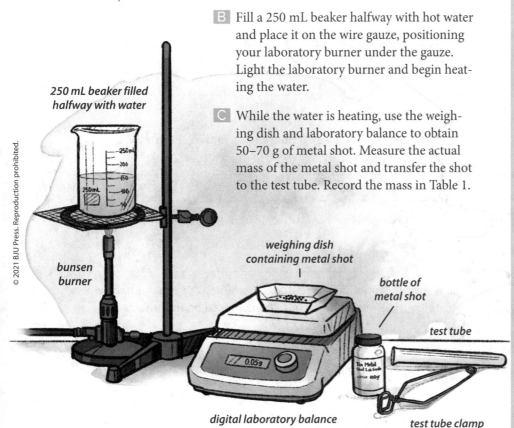

250 mL beaker filled halfway with water

bunsen burner

weighing dish containing metal shot

bottle of metal shot

test tube

0.05 g

digital laboratory balance

test tube clamp

Setup for heating metal shot in a hot-water bath

Heating Up

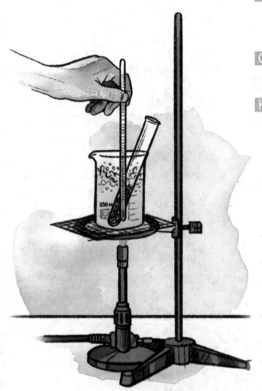

D Place the test tube into the beaker of water and bring the water to a boil.

1. How do you think the temperature of the metal shot will be affected during heating?

_____

_____

_____

E While the metal sample is heating, measure the combined mass of the two foam cups and record the value in Table 1. These cups will be used to construct your calorimeter.

F Using the graduated cylinder, measure about 50 mL of distilled water into the inner cup and weigh the cups and the water. Record this mass in Table 1.

G Calculate the mass of water that is in your calorimeter and record your answer in Table 1.

H After the water in the beaker has boiled for at least 10 minutes, measure the temperature of the water. Be sure to hold the thermometer in the center of the beaker. Record this temperature as the initial temperature of the metal in Table 1.

2. Will the metal shot gain or lose thermal energy in the calorimeter? Explain.

_____

_____

3. Will the water gain or lose thermal energy in the calorimeter? Explain.

_____

_____

4. Write a word equation that relates the heat of the water and the heat of the metal.

_____

5. Substitute the formula for thermal energy into your equation, remembering to keep the water on one side and the metal on the other.

6. Rearrange this equation to solve for the specific heat of the metal. This is what you are looking for! Show your work in the margin if needed.

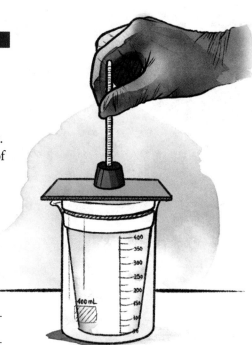

USING THE CALORIMETER

I Nest the two foam cups together, and place them inside the 400 mL beaker for added stability as shown at right.

J While wearing the puncture-proof gloves, insert the thermometer into the split rubber stopper, using a drop or two of liquid soap to lubricate it. Adjust the position of the stopper on the thermometer so that the bulb of the thermometer does not touch the bottom of the inner cup when it is inserted through the hole in the cardboard lid (used in Step L).

K Measure the initial temperature of the water in the calorimeter and record it in Table 1.

7. Do you need to convert between the Celsius scale and the Kelvin scale for this activity? Explain.

_____

_____

_____

L Using the test tube clamp, remove the test tube from the boiling water and quickly pour the metal shot into the calorimeter. Be careful not to get any drops of hot water into the calorimeter or to splash water from the calorimeter when you pour in the metal shot! Cover the top with a cardboard lid and swirl the mixture carefully.

M Note the temperature of the water about every 30 seconds and measure the highest temperature reached. Record this final temperature of both the metal and the water in Table 1.

8. At this point, what has happened to the flow of thermal energy?

_____

_____

9. Consider the change in temperature. Did the water and metal do what you anticipated in Questions 2 and 3?

_____

_____

N Carefully decant into the sink as much water as possible without losing any metal shot. Pour the wet metal shot into the designated container so that it can dry.

RUBBER STOPPERS AND BROKEN THERMOMETERS

Be sure that you wear gloves and exercise caution when inserting the thermometer into the split rubber stopper. Use soap as a lubricant, and don't put a force on the thermometer that could cause it to break.

10. Use your data from Table 1 and the rearranged equation to solve for the specific heat of the metal. Show your work.

11. Using the accepted value for the specific heat of the metal supplied by your teacher, calculate the percent error for your experimental value.

12. List three possible sources of error in your experiment.

_____

_____

_____

_____

13. Determine whether the errors you mentioned in Question 12 would result in an experimental value for the specific heat value that was larger or smaller than expected. Explain why it would have this effect.

_____

_____

_____

_____

Going Further

Maybe you are not used to thinking about heat as something that can be productive! Heat transfer can be very useful because it can be used to generate electricity. This usually happens when heat is used to generate steam, which can turn a turbine.

14. Suggest some ways that heat transfer can be used to generate steam for electricity generation.

_____

_____

_____

Heat can also be a waste product. When factories put out heated air or heated water, it can cause problems in the environment.

15. Suggest some problems that waste heat can cause in the environment.

_____

_____

_____

16. Suggest a way to deal with waste heat.

_____

_____

_____

17. Most factories produce large quantities of heat, and many facilities operate around the clock. Explain how an engineer would use a calculation similar to that used in this activity to determine how to use water as the coolant for a factory.

_____

_____

_____

TABLE 1

	Mass (g)	T_i (°C)	T_f (°C)	c_{sp} (J/g·°C)
Metal (T_i for Metal)				
Cups				
Cups and Water				
Water				

15B LAB

No Anchovies, Please!

QUESTIONS

» How do I determine an enthalpy of solution?

» How can I find the enthalpy of reaction for a particular chemical reaction?

Exploring Enthalpies of Solution and Reaction

Pizza is a favorite among students. Some college students practically live on pizza! Pizzas come in all shapes and sizes, and people love to pile on the toppings, such as pepperoni, mushrooms, and even anchovies. Pizza is a great source of energy for late-night study sessions. How do our bodies turn that food into energy? Through digestion. Digestion is a combined physical and chemical process by which humans and animals obtain energy. Chemical digestion uses chemical reactions to break chemical bonds, releasing energy. Our bodies use that energy for all sorts of metabolic functions. Any energy that is not used is stored for a later time.

Ideally we want to balance our energy intake with our energy usage because we don't need to be storing too much energy. To do that, we should eat balanced meals, so living on pizza through college is probably not in our best interest. How can we measure the energy transfer during chemical and physical changes? We use calorimetry, the same process that you may recall using in Lab 15A.

In this lab activity, you will find the enthalpy of two different processes: the enthalpy of solution of potassium nitrate (KNO_3) and the enthalpy of reaction of hydrochloric acid (HCl) with magnesium. The thermal energy changes that you measure in your calorimeter are the enthalpy when the pressure is held constant.

$$Q = \Delta H$$

You'll need to do some calculations to make sure that your units are correct since enthalpy is measured in kJ/mol.

How can I measure the energy change during physical and chemical changes?

EQUIPMENT

- laboratory balance
- foam cups, 6–8 oz (2)
- beaker, 600 mL
- thermometer
- split rubber stopper, 1-hole, #4
- cardboard, 10 × 10 cm
- graduated cylinder, 100 mL
- room-temperature distilled water
- weighing dish
- potassium nitrate (KNO_3), solid
- hydrochloric acid (HCl), 1.00 M
- magnesium ribbon, 0.10–0.15 g
- goggles
- laboratory apron
- nitrile gloves
- puncture-proof gloves

Procedure

A Nest the two foam cups together, and place them inside the 600 mL glass beaker for added stability as shown at right.

B While wearing the puncture-proof gloves, insert the thermometer into the split rubber stopper, using a drop or two of liquid soap to lubricate it. Adjust the position of the stopper on the thermometer so that the bulb of the thermometer does not touch the bottom of the inner cup when it is inserted through the hole in the cardboard lid (used in Step H). Set the thermometer, rubber stopper, and cardboard aside.

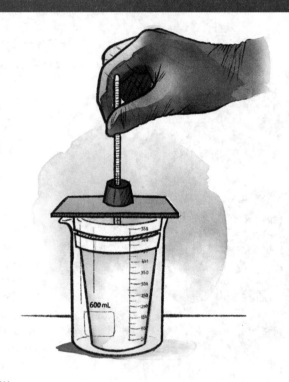

RUBBER STOPPERS AND BROKEN THERMOMETERS

Be sure that you wear gloves and exercise caution when inserting the thermometer into the split rubber stopper. Use soap as a lubricant, and don't put a force on the thermometer that could cause it to break.

HEAT OF SOLUTION

C Measure the mass of the nested foam cups and record the value in Tables 1 and 2.

D Using the graduated cylinder, measure about 50 mL of distilled water into the inner cup and measure the mass of the cups and water. Record the mass in Table 1.

E Calculate the mass of water that you are using in your calorimeter and record it in Table 1.

F Determine the temperature of this water to the nearest 0.1 °C and record it in Table 1. Be sure that the thermometer bulb is in the center of the water sample.

G Using the weighing dish and laboratory balance, obtain 3–4 g of KNO_3. Record the actual mass of KNO_3 in Table 1.

WEIGHING WEIGHING PAPER?

If you have an electronic balance, tare or zero the balance with the weighing paper on it before adding KNO_3 so that you don't need to weigh the weighing paper and reweigh it with the KNO_3 on it.

1. Write a balanced chemical equation that shows the dissolving process of KNO_3. Don't include the water in the equation since it just makes the salt dissociate.

_____

H Add the KNO_3 to the water and cover your calorimeter with the cardboard lid. Swirl the calorimeter gently while closely observing the temperature.

I Watch the temperature over a period of several minutes and record the most extreme temperature in Table 1.

2. Did the dissolving process release heat or absorb it?

_____

_____

Since ΔH_{soln} is expressed as J/mol (or kJ/mol), you must calculate the thermal energy and the moles of KNO_3 and then divide those answers to get J/mol.

3. Calculate the thermal energy change of the water. Show your work. Record your answer in Table 1.

4. Does the energy change of the water indicate that the dissolving of potassium chloride absorbs energy or releases energy? Explain.

_____

_____

_____

The temperature of the solution changed because the potassium nitrate broke up into ions. The change in temperature of the water also gives us the change in temperature of the KNO_3.

5. Now calculate the moles of KNO_3 that dissolved in the water.

6. Using the appropriate sign—positive for endothermic or negative for exothermic—express the enthalpy in kJ/mol. Record your answer in Table 1.

7. Calculate a percent error on the basis of the standard value for the enthalpy of solution of KNO_3. This value is $\Delta H^\circ_{sol} = +34.89$ kJ/mol. Record your answer in Table 1.

8. Is your value for enthalpy positive or negative? How does this relate to your observations in Question 3?

_____

_____

HEAT OF REACTION

The next reaction generates minimal hydrogen gas because you are using a fairly dilute hydrochloric acid. Nevertheless, make sure that there are no open flames nearby when doing this activity.

J Empty the calorimeter, rinse well with water, and allow to drain.

K Using the graduated cylinder, measure 75.0 mL of 1.00 M HCl solution and pour it into the inner cup. Measure the mass of the cups and hydrochloric acid, then calculate the mass of the acid alone. Record both masses in Table 2.

L Measure the temperature of the HCl in the cup and record it in Table 2.

M Measure the mass of the magnesium ribbon and record it in Table 2.

N Roll the magnesium ribbon into a loose ball, drop it into the acid, and cover the cup.

This is an example of what happens when a metal reacts with a strong acid. This process usually liberates hydrogen gas and forms a salt with the anion of the acid and an ionized form of the metal, which will be a cation.

O While gently swirling the cup, observe the temperature constantly. The metal should react completely. Record the most extreme temperature reached in Table 2.

9. What did you observe during this reaction?

_____

_____

_____

10. Write a balanced equation that shows the reaction of HCl with Mg to liberate hydrogen gas and form a salt.

_____

Now calculate the theoretical enthalpy of the reaction.

11. Use the balanced equation and the standard values shown at right to calculate the enthalpy of reaction between HCl and Mg. Show your work.

ENTHALPIES OF
FORMATION FOR
QUESTION 11

HCl (*aq*): $\Delta H_f^\circ = -167.2$ kJ/mol

Mg (*s*): $\Delta H_f^\circ = -641.8$ kJ/mol

12. Calculate the thermal energy change of the HCl (assume that c_{sp} is the same as water) that actually happened. Record your answer in Table 2.

13. Since the reaction occurred in the solution, does this change indicate that the reaction is endothermic or exothermic? Explain.

_____

_____

The magnesium was the limiting reactant for this reaction.

14. Calculate the moles of Mg that reacted. Show your work. Record your answer in Table 2.

15. Express the enthalpy in kJ/mol. Record your answer in Table 2.

16. Calculate a percent error using the enthalpy of reaction that you calculated in Question 12. Record your answer in Table 2.

17. Is your value for enthalpy positive or negative? How does this relate to your observations from Questions 9 and 11?

_____

_____

Going Further

On a small scale, people use the reaction of a metal such as copper with sulfuric acid and iron(III) chloride in a process called *photo etching*. This basically allows people to "print" a circuit that can be used in a circuit board. During this process, the acid is heated to speed up the reaction.

18. Why does heating the acid speed up the process?

_____

_____

19. Suggest another way to use the process of etching.

_____

_____

_____

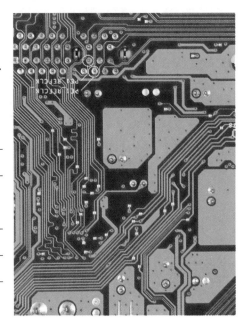

TABLE 1 *Enthalpy of Solution*

	Mass (g)	Temperature (°C)	Energy (J)	ΔHsol (kJ/mol)	%$_{error}$
Cups					
Cups and Water					
Water (T_i)					
KNO$_3$					
KNO$_3$ Solution (T_f)					

TABLE 2 *Enthalpy of Reaction*

	Mass (g)	Moles	Temperature (°C)	Energy (J)	ΔH$_r$ (kJ/mol)	%$_{error}$
Cups						
Cups and HCl						
HCl (at T_i)						
Magnesium Ribbon						
HCl (at T_f)						

16A LAB

Name _____

Date _____

EQUIPMENT

- beakers, 100 mL (6)
- beakers, 200 mL (3)
- grease pencil or labeling tape
- graduated cylinders, 25 mL (3)
- stirring rod
- stopwatch
- sodium thiosulfate $(Na_2S_2O_3)$, 0.20 M, 100 mL
- distilled water, 100 mL
- hydrochloric acid (HCl), 1.0 M, 175 mL
- sodium thiosulfate $(Na_2S_2O_3)$, x M, 25 mL
- goggles
- laboratory apron
- nitrile gloves

Chemistry—A Contact Sport?

Exploring Concentration's Effect on Reaction Rates

Rugby is clearly a contact sport. Two variants of the game are rubgy sevens and rugby union. While both variants are played on the same-size field, the number of players differs significantly. In rugby union, each team has fifteen players on the field, while in rugby sevens there are only seven players per team. As you can imagine, there are a whole lot more collisions on the field in a rugby union game.

Chemistry is similar to a contact sport. According to the collision theory, a chemical reaction will occur only if particles collide, and when they collide they must do so with enough force and in the proper orientation. If there are more particles present, we would expect more reactions to occur.

The speed at which the reaction proceeds is its rate. *Rate* can also be defined as either the amount of product formed per unit of time or the amount of reactant consumed per unit of time. In this experiment, you will explore how varying the concentration of a reactant affects how fast a reaction takes place.

How does concentration affect reaction rate?

QUESTIONS

» How do the concentrations of reactants affect the reaction rate?

» Once I know the rate law, can I determine the concentration of a reactant on the basis of the reaction time?

Procedure

A Check that your beakers are clean and dry.

B Using the grease pencil or labeling tape, label five of the 100 mL beakers 1 through 5. Label a sixth beaker "Unknown."

C Label the 200 mL beakers "$Na_2S_2O_3$," "distilled water," and "HCl." Obtain 100 mL each of $Na_2S_2O_3$ and distilled water and 175 mL of HCl.

D In Beakers 1–5, prepare mixtures of varying concentration amounts by combining sodium thiosulfate and distilled water in the proportions shown in Table 1. Use a different graduated cylinder for the sodium thiosulfate and the water. Stir each mixture thoroughly, rinsing and drying the stirring rod before stirring subsequent mixtures.

1. When making the mixtures of the sodium thiosulfate solutions and water, why was it important that the test tubes have no water in them?

_____

_____

_____

The reaction that you will use is a redox reaction between the thiosulfate ion, $S_2O_3^{2-}$, supplied by the sodium thiosulfate, $Na_2S_2O_3$, and the hydrogen ion supplied by the hydrochloric acid, HCl. The sodium and chloride ions are spectator ions in this reaction. The two reactants produce elemental sulfur, sulfur dioxide, and water.

2. Write a balanced equation that shows this reaction.

_____

3. Elemental sulfur is a nonpolar substance. Do you think it is soluble in water? Explain.

_____

_____

4. How do you think you will know when the reaction begins?

_____

_____

_____

5. How do you think you can consistently measure the reaction time if the concentration changes the reaction rate?

_____

_____

_____

_____

E Set Beaker 1 on the image of the T on the right. You should be able to see the T as you look down through the solution.

F Use the remaining graduated cylinder to add 25.0 mL of 1.0 M hydrochloric acid to Beaker 1 and start the stopwatch. Stop timing once the T is no longer visible. Record the time in Table 1.

G Repeat Steps E and F for Beakers 2–5.

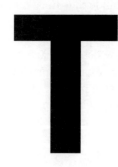

CREATING A MODEL

H Calculate the moles of thiosulfate ion, $S_2O_3^{2-}$, for Beakers 1–5. Show your work for Beaker 1 below and record all your results in Table 1.

I Calculate the amount concentration of $S_2O_3^{2-}$ using the total volume in each beaker, including the volume of 1.0 M HCl. Show your work for Beaker 1 below and record all your results in Table 1.

J Create a scatterplot of the amount concentration of $S_2O_3^{2-}$ and reaction time. Include a curve of best fit.

6. What happens to the time required for the reaction and the rate of the reaction as the concentration of the thiosulfate ion increases?

_____

_____

7. On the basis of the collision theory, explain why this relationship makes sense.

_____

_____

_____

8. If the relationship between amount concentration and reaction time is correct, what is the relationship between amount concentration and reaction rate? Explain.

_____

_____

_____

_____

9. According to your scatterplot, how long would the reaction take if using a 0.15 M solution? if using a 0.01 M solution?

_____

_____

TESTING AN UNKNOWN

K Pour a 25.0 mL sample of a solution of $Na_2S_2O_3$ of unknown molarity into the clean, dry beaker marked "Unknown."

L Set the beaker on the image of the T.

M Using the graduated cylinder for the HCl, add 25 mL of HCl to the unknown and start timing. Stop timing once the T is no longer visible. Record the time in Table 2.

10. Using your scatterplot, estimate the concentration of thiosulfate in your unknown solution.

_____

_____

11. Get the actual amount concentration from your teacher. Record this value in Table 2 and calculate your percent error. Show your work below and record your results in Table 2.

12. Look at the six beakers. Has any sulfur settled out? What does the answer to that question indicate?

_____

13. As shown by your scatterplot, where is the reaction time more sensitive to changes in amount concentration? Why do you think this is true?

_____

_____

_____

Going Further

In 2009 there was a fire at a nightclub in Perm, Russia. Over 100 people died as the burning insulation released cyanide. Many of the deaths and hospitalizations related to this accident were a result of cyanide poisoning.

Sodium thiosulfate can be administered intravenously to patients who experience both arsenic and cyanide poisoning. Increasing the concentration allows a patient's body to eliminate the cyanide as the sodium thiosulfate binds to the cyanide and helps it pass harmlessly through the body.

14. How does this example of chemical kinetics work to alleviate people's suffering?

_____

_____

TABLE 1 *Data*

Beaker	Volume $Na_2S_2O_3$ (mL)	Volume Water (mL)	Volume HCl (mL)	Total Volume (mL)	Reaction Time (s)	Moles $S_2O_3^{2-}$	Amount Concentration $S_2O_3^{2-}$ (mol/L)
1	25.0	0.0	25.0	50.0			
2	20.0	5.0	25.0	50.0			
3	15.0	10.0	25.0	50.0			
4	10.0	15.0	25.0	50.0			
5	5.0	20.0	25.0	50.0			

TABLE 2 *Testing an Unknown*

Reaction Time (s)	Predicted Amount Concentration (mol/L)	Actual Amount Concentration (mol/L)	Percent Error

Name _____

Date _____

Don't Overreact

Determining a Rate Law

We all understand that iron rusts slowly, while methane burns rapidly. Every reaction proceeds at its own rate. But we also understand that under different conditions, each individual reaction will proceed at different rates.

Chemists use reaction rate laws to describe how specific reactions respond to the concentration of the reactants. Rate laws can be determined only empirically.

How can we determine the rate law for a chemical reaction?

In this lab activity we will study the reaction between potassium iodide, potassium bromate, and hydrochloric acid. Iodide, bromate, and hydrogen ions react to form molecular iodine, free bromide ions, and water.

$$6KI(aq) + KBrO_3(aq) + 6HCl(aq) \longrightarrow$$
$$3I_2(aq) + 6KCl(aq) + KBr(aq) + 3H_2O(l)$$

Eliminating the spectator ions—K^+ and Cl^-—yields the net ionic equation.

$$6I^-(aq) + BrO_3^-(aq) + 6H^+(aq) \longrightarrow 3I_2(aq) + Br^-(aq) + 3H_2O(l)$$

To create a time delay in the reaction, we will also include thiosulfate ions, which react quickly with molecular iodine according to the following equation.

$$I_2(aq) + 2S_2O_3^{2-}(aq) \longrightarrow 2I^-(aq) + S_4O_6^{2-}(aq)$$

To indicate the "stop" point of our reaction, we will include some starch solution in the reaction vessel. Once all the thiosulfate ions are consumed, the molecular iodine will combine with the starch to form a black complex. The general form of the rate law for this reaction is shown below.

$$rate = k[I^-]^l \left[BrO_3^-\right]^m [H^+]^n$$

Note that l, m, and n are the reaction orders for the three ions.

In this lab activity you will vary the concentration of each ion to see its effect on reaction rate. From this information you will be able to determine the reaction rate, the reaction order for each ion, and the constant k for the temperature at which you conduct the trials.

QUESTION

» What affects the rate law?

EQUIPMENT

- beakers, 100 mL (7)
- graduated cylinders, 10 mL (2)
- graduated cylinders, 25 mL (4)
- stopwatch
- disposable pipette
- grease pencil or labeling tape
- potassium iodide solution, 0.010 M, 80 mL
- potassium bromate, 0.040 M, 80 mL
- sodium thiosulfate solution, 0.000 25 M, 80 mL
- hydrochloric acid, 0.10 M, 80 mL
- distilled water, 80 mL
- starch solution, 5 mL
- goggles
- laboratory apron
- nitrile gloves

Procedure

A Label the beakers "KI," "KBrO$_3$," "Na$_2$S$_2$O$_3$," "HCl," "Water," "A," and "B."

B Label the 10 mL graduated cylinders "S" for starch and "T" for sodium thiosulfate.

C Label the 25 mL graduated cylinders "KI" for potassium iodide, "Br" for potassium bromate, "H" for hydrochloric acid, and "W" for water.

D Fill the appropriately labeled beakers with 80 mL of potassium iodide, potassium bromate, sodium thiosulfate, hydrochloric acid, and distilled water.

E Using Cylinder S, obtain approximately 5 mL of starch solution.

Table 1 indicates the volume of each solution needed in each trial. As you would expect, you will be changing the volume of the potassium iodide, potassium bromate, and hydrochloric acid. These changes allow you to check the effect that changing concentration has on reaction rate.

TABLE 1 *Volumes*

Beaker A			
Trial	Volume KI (mL)	Volume Na$_2$S$_2$O$_3$ (mL)	Volume H$_2$O (mL)
1	10.0	9.0	10.0
2	20.0	9.0	0.0
3	10.0	9.0	0.0
4	10.0	9.0	0.0

Beaker B			
Volume KBrO$_3$ (mL)	Volume HCl (mL)	Starch (mL)	Total Volume (mL)
10.0	10.0	1.0	50.0
10.0	10.0	1.0	50.0
20.0	10.0	1.0	50.0
10.0	20.0	1.0	50.0

1. Why do you think the water volume changes in the different trials?

_____

_____

_____

_____

_____

F Calculate the moles of each ion provided by the volume indicated for Trial 1. Show your work for iodide below.

G Using your answer from Step F, calculate the amount concentration of each ion in Trial 1. Remember that the amount concentration is affected by the total volume. Show your work for iodide below and record your answers in Table 2.

H Repeat Steps F–G for the remaining trials. Record these values in Table 2.

I In Beaker A, mix the appropriate volumes from Table 1 of the potassium iodide, sodium thiosulfate, and distilled water.

J In Beaker B, mix the appropriate volumes (see Trial 1 of Table 2) of the potassium bromate, hydrochloric acid, and starch solution.

K Pour the contents from Beaker B into Beaker A and start the stopwatch. Pour the entire mixture back into Beaker B to ensure complete mixing.

L Stop timing when the solution turns blue and record the time in Table 3.

M Clean Beakers A and B and dry completely in preparation for the remaining trials.

2. Why is it so important to dry the beakers between trials?

_____

_____

_____

N Repeat Steps I–M for the volumes of solutions from Table 1 for Trials 2–4.

3. Consider the values for the amount concentration of each substance. Explain what we are testing in each of Trials 2–4.

_____

_____

_____

_____

_____

4. Why does the concentration of thiosulfate ions not vary in any of the trials?

_____

_____

_____

_____

_____

_____

O For Trial 2, calculate the change in concentration by determining the ratio of the new concentration to the original concentration for the iodide ions. Record this value in Table 3.

P For Trial 2, calculate the change in reaction rate by determining the ratio of the original reaction time to the new reaction time. Record this value in Table 3.

5. Notice that in Steps O and P we calculated a ratio. In Step O we found the change in concentration by dividing the new value by the original. But in Step P we found the change in rate by dividing the original by the new. Why do you think this change was made to calculate the change in rate?

_____

_____

_____

Recall that the reaction orders are the exponents on each concentration in the rate law. For example, a reaction order of 0 is indicated by no change in the reaction rate when the concentration is changed. A reaction order of 1 (linear) means that the reaction rate changes by the same factor as the change in concentration. So if the concentration doubles, the reaction rate doubles also. Reaction orders of 2 (quadratic) indicate that the reaction rate will change by a square of the change in concentration. In other words, if we double the concentration, the reaction rate will be four times faster.

Q For Trial 2, determine the reaction order for iodide ions by comparing the change in concentration to the change in reaction rate. Record the reaction order in Table 3.

R Repeat Steps O–P for the bromate in Trial 3 and the hydrogen ions in Trial 4. Record these values in Table 3.

Going Further

Recall that the rate law for this reaction has the form shown below.

$$rate = k[I^-]^l[BrO_3^-]^m[H^+]^n$$

We have determined the reaction orders for each of the reactants. Now we want to determine the k value for the temperature at which you did your trials. To do this we are going to solve the rate law for k.

$$k = \frac{rate}{[I^-]^l[BrO_3^-]^m[H^+]^n}$$

In order to solve for k, we need to know the rate. Remember that we included thiosulfate to provide an indication of the reaction. We can use the concentration of thiosulfate to determine the rate of reaction.

$$rate = \frac{[S_2O_3^{2-}]}{6\,t_{reaction}}$$

The $[S_2O_3^{2-}]$ should make sense because our indication of reaction completion was when the thiosulfate was consumed. And the reaction time should also make sense as this is the time that the reaction took. The 6 in the equation comes from the two ionic equations at the beginning of the lab activity. Each occurrence of the first reaction produces three iodine molecules, and each of the iodine molecules consumes two thiosulfate ions. Therefore, the thiosulfate is consumed six times for each occurrence of the primary reaction.

S Calculate the reaction rate for each trial and record it in Table 3.

T Calculate the k value for each trial and record it in Table 3.

6. How consistent were your values for the constant k?

_____

_____

_____

7. How can you explain the consistency of your values for the constant k?

_____

_____

_____

8. Describe some situations where it may be important to understand reaction rates and what influences them.

_____

_____

_____

_____

_____

TABLE 2 *Concentrations*

Trial	$[I^-]$ (M)	$[S_2O_3^{2-}]$ (M)	$[BrO_3^-]$ (M)	$[H^+]$ (M)
1				
2				
3				
4				

TABLE 3 *Results*

Trial	Changed Substance X	$t_{reaction}$ (s)	$\Delta[X]$	$\Delta Rate_{reaction}$	Reaction Order	$Rate_{reaction}$ ($\times 10^{-7}$)	k
1							
2	I^-						
3	BrO_3^-						
4	H^+						

17A LAB

Stressed Out

Inquiring into Le Châtelier's Principle

Personal space—people typically feel strongly about it. When someone moves into what we consider our personal space, we tend to feel uncomfortable and make adjustments to alleviate the stress that we feel.

Chemical systems do something similar. A reversible chemical reaction will reach equilibrium when the forward and reverse reactions are occurring simultaneously at the same rate. The amounts of reactants and products remain constant, a condition called the *equilibrium position*. But what happens when we interfere with a system at equilibrium? Just like when someone invades our personal space, a chemical system will adjust itself to reduce the change that was imposed upon it. This is what chemists call *Le Châtelier's principle*.

In this inquiry lab activity you will investigate the effect of varying conditions on the equilibrium position of a chemical reaction involving solutions of iron(III) chloride and potassium thiocyanate.

How do chemical systems respond to changing conditions?

QUESTIONS

» What does a chemical reaction in equilibrium look like?

» How can I test the effect of different stresses on a chemical reaction in equilibrium?

» How can I predict the change in the equilibrium position of a reaction due to stresses that I put on the system?

EQUIPMENT

- test tubes (2)
- test tube rack
- Erlenmeyer flask, 250 mL
- pipettes (2)
- labeling tape or grease pencil
- iron(III) chloride (FeCl$_3$), 0.25 M, 5 mL
- potassium thiocyanate (KSCN), 0.25 M, 5 mL
- distilled water, 100 mL
- goggles
- laboratory apron
- nitrile gloves

Procedure

PLANNING/WRITING SCIENTIFIC QUESTIONS

A Label the test tubes "Fe" for iron(III) chloride and "K" for potassium thiocyanate.

B Obtain approximately 5 mL each of iron(III) chloride and potassium thiocyanate in the test tubes. Observe the two solutions. Put a pipette in each of the two tubes.

C Fill the Erlenmeyer flask with 100 mL of distilled water, then add 5 drops of each of the solutions. Mix thoroughly and observe.

1. Write the balanced chemical equation between iron(III) chloride and potassium thiocyanate.

_____

D Research the two products to determine which is producing the color observed.

E Brainstorm with your lab group about how you can disrupt the equilibrium of the system.

F Write specific questions related to chemical equilibrium that you could answer by collecting data.

DESIGNING SCIENTIFIC INVESTIGATIONS

G Write procedures to collect data that will allow you to answer the questions that you wrote in Step F above.

H Have your teacher approve your procedures.

CONDUCTING SCIENTIFIC INVESTIGATIONS

I Following the procedures that you have written, collect the data to answer the questions that you wrote.

DEVELOPING MODELS

J Develop a matrix of possible changes to the system and the effect of each of those changes.

SCIENTIFIC ARGUMENTATION

K Explain what you know about the reaction between iron(III) chloride and potassium thiocyanate. Support your claims with evidence from the data collected.

17B LAB

Name _____

Date _____

Precipitous Changes

Exploring Solubility Products

Water is a precious commodity. It is also a key medium for many industrial processes, during which it may become contaminated. How do we clean the water used in these processes to protect this vital resource?

How can we change the substance that precipitates from a chemical reaction?

Chemists often use chemical precipitation to clean the water used in industrial processes. By chemically treating the water, they can force hazardous compounds out of solution. These compounds can then be filtered from the water.

In this lab activity you will investigate solubility products and how they are related to solubility of solutes in solution and to the formation of precipitates.

QUESTIONS

» How can I make some of a precipitate go away when the solution is saturated?

» How can I determine the concentration of a saturated solution?

EQUIPMENT

- beakers, 50 mL (3)
- graduated cylinders, 10 mL (3)
- graduated cylinders, 25 mL (3)
- weighing dishes (2)
- stirring rod
- test tubes (2)
- test tube rack
- sodium sulfide (Na_2S) solution, 0.1 M
- distilled water
- silver nitrate ($AgNO_3$), 0.43 g
- sodium chloride (NaCl), 0.15 g
- labeling tape or grease pencil
- goggles
- laboratory apron

Procedure

SETTING UP

A Label three beakers and three 10 mL graduated cylinders each for silver nitrate, sodium chloride, and sodium sulfide.

B Pour approximately 25 mL of the sodium sulfide solution into its beaker.

C Use one of the 25 mL graduated cylinders to add 25.0 mL of distilled water to each of the other two beakers.

D Using one of the weighing dishes, add 0.43 g of $AgNO_3$ to its beaker and stir until all the solid is dissolved. Using the other weighing dish, add 0.15 g of NaCl to its beaker and stir until all the solid is dissolved. Be sure to clean and dry the stirring rod between stirring the two solutions.

E Label the two test tubes "A" and "B."

1. Write the balanced equations for the dissolving of $AgNO_3$ and NaCl.

_____

_____

F Calculate the amount concentration of the $AgNO_3$ and NaCl solutions that you have made. Show your work for $AgNO_3$ below and record your answers for both calculations in Table 1.

G Using the appropriate graduated cylinders, transfer 10 mL each of the silver nitrate and sodium chloride solutions to both Tube A and Tube B.

2. What are your observations of the reaction in Tube A?

_____

_____

3. Write the balanced chemical equation for combining the silver nitrate and the sodium chloride solutions.

_____

4. Write ionic and net ionic equations for combining the silver nitrate and sodium chloride solutions.

5. Why did a precipitate form?

_____

_____

6. Without looking up the solubility or K_{sp} values for silver chloride, what can you conclude about them?

_____

_____

_____

_____

_____

 Look up the K_{sp} value for silver chloride and record it in Table 1.

7. Was your prediction in Question 5 correct?

_____

8. On the basis of the K_{sp} value for silver chloride, calculate the solubility of the solution in Tube A.

9. Look back at the ionic equation in Question 3. What will be the effect on the equilibrium of the system if you were to add sodium sulfide solution to Tube B? Explain.

_____

_____

_____

_____

_____

 Using the appropriate graduated cylinder, transfer 10 mL of sodium sulfide solution to Tube B.

10. What are your observations of the reaction in Tube B?

_____

_____

_____

_____

11. Did the reaction behave as expected? Explain.

_____

_____

_____

12. On the basis of your observations, how do you expect the K_{sp} value for silver sulfide to compare with the value for silver chloride? Explain.

_____

_____

_____

_____

_____

J Look up the K_{sp} value for silver sulfide and record it in Table 1.

13. On the basis of the K_{sp} value for silver sulfide, calculate the solubility of the solution in Tube A.

•

Going Further

14. How could we use solubility and solubility products to benefit people?

_____

_____

_____

_____

_____

TABLE 1

Initial [AgNO$_3$]	
Initial [NaCl]	
K_{sp} Silver Chloride	
K_{sp} Silver Sulfide	
Final [AgCl]	
Final [Ag$_2$S]	

Name _____

Date _____

Colorful Chemistry

Exploring Acid-Base Indicators

Indicators are chemical substances that are used to indicate the presence or concentration of another chemical. You probably think that indicators exist only in laboratories. But they're actually everywhere! Many acid-base indicators occur naturally in the world around us. The leaves of red cabbage, the flowers of geraniums and poppies, the stems of rhubarb, and the fruit of blueberries, cherries, and black currants all contain chemicals that can indicate acids or bases. Litmus, a very common laboratory indicator, comes from lichen! With the right combination of indicators, you can cover the whole pH spectrum. Of course, pH meters give you a more accurate and objective reading of pH, but indicators are useful because they are more widely available.

How does amount concentration of weak acids affect pH?

Acid-base indicators (identified by "In" in the equation below) are generally weak organic acids or bases that exist in equilibrium between the conjugate acid-base pair. Each member of the pair has a different color. The equation below shows this.

$$HIn(aq) + H_2O(l) \rightleftharpoons H_3O^+(aq) + In^-(aq)$$

color 1   color 2

According to Le Châtelier's principle, changes in the concentration of H_3O^+ will shift the equilibrium, affecting the color of the indicator. When the color changes, we can know what's happening to the hydronium concentration of the solution.

In this experiment, you'll try your hand at making a rainbow of chemistry. You will make three sets of standards. Each set will cover a range of five concentrations and will contain an acid-base indicator. You'll use these colors to estimate the hydronium ion concentration and pH of some solutions.

QUESTIONS

» What do indicators do?

» How can I estimate how acidic a solution is?

» How can I measure the concentration of an acid?

EQUIPMENT

- pH meter
- test tubes (21)
- test tube racks (2)
- graduated cylinder, 100 mL
- graduated cylinder, 10 mL
- transfer pipettes (3)
- labeling tape or grease pencil
- hydrochloric acid (HCl), 0.1 M
- distilled water
- thymol blue solution
- methyl orange solution
- methyl red solution
- acetic acid ($HC_2H_3O_2$), 0.1 M
- unknown weak acid
- goggles
- laboratory apron
- nitrile gloves

Procedure

A. Label five test tubes "1A" through "1E," five test tubes "2A" through "2E," and five test tubes "3A" through "3E." Place them in the test tube racks.

B. Measure 15 mL of 0.1 M HCl solution in the 100 mL graduated cylinder.

C. Using the 10 mL graduated cylinder, transfer 3 mL portions of the HCl into Tubes 1A, 2A, and 3A. You should have 6 mL of 0.1 M HCl remaining in the 100 mL graduated cylinder.

D. Add distilled water to the 100 mL graduated cylinder up to a total of 60 mL and mix well. This dilutes the acid to 0.01 M HCl. ***Normally we don't add water to acid because the acid can splatter. But in this setting, you are using extremely dilute acids, which eliminates the risk.***

E. Rinse the 10 mL graduated cylinder thoroughly and then pour 3 mL portions of the 0.01 M HCl into Tubes 1B, 2B, and 3B.

F. Repeat Steps D and E to make the solutions listed in Table 1, pouring 3 mL portions of the HCl solutions into the appropriate test tubes as specified below.

0.001 M HCl in Tubes 1C, 2C, and 3C

0.0001 M HCl in Tubes 1D, 2D, and 3D

0.00001 M HCl in Tubes 1E, 2E, and 3E

G. For each solution in Tubes 1A–1E, use one of the pipettes to add three drops of thymol blue solution. Swirl the solutions well and record the color of each in Table 2.

TABLE 1

HCl	Thymol Blue	Methyl Orange	Methyl Red
0.1 M	1A	2A	3A
0.01 M	1B	2B	3B
0.001 M	1C	2C	3C
0.0001 M	1D	2D	3D
0.000 01 M	1E	2E	3E

Thymol blue is an artificial indicator that can undergo two color changes. From left to right, these structures produce blue in basic solutions, orange in neutral solutions, and red in acids. Study these three structures to see how the structure changes with each color change.

blue
(in bases)

orange
(in neutral solutions)

red
(in acids)

1. In the image shown above, how does the structure of thymol blue change, as indicated by a color change?

_____

_____

2. Which structure do you have in your test tubes right now? How can you tell?

_____

_____

H For Tubes 2A–2E, use a second pipette to add three drops of methyl orange solution. Swirl the solutions well and record the color of each in Table 2.

I For Tubes 3A–3E, use the third pipette to add three drops of methyl red solution. Swirl the solutions well and record the color of each in Table 2.

J Use a pH probe to measure the exact pH of your dilutions in all fifteen tubes to the nearest 0.1. Make sure that you rinse the probe between tests. If a pH probe is not available, calculate the pH from $[H_3O^+]$. Record these values in Table 2.

3. What effect does a dilution by a factor of 10 have on the pH of an HCl solution?

_____

4. On the basis of your answer to Question 3, describe how easy it is to change the pH of a solution?

_____

_____

5. Estimate the pH range over which each of the indicators changes color.

_____

_____

Now you are going to use the indicator standards that you just created to learn more about the pH range in which they work best.

COMPARING HC₂H₃O₂ TO STANDARDS

K Label three test tubes "4," "5," and "6." Using the 10 mL graduated cylinder, measure 3.0 mL of 0.1 M $HC_2H_3O_2$ solution into these test tubes.

L Add three drops of thymol blue solution to Tube 4, three drops of methyl orange solution to Tube 5, and three drops of methyl red solution to Tube 6.

M Compare the colors in Tubes 4–6 with the appropriate indicator standards in Tubes 1A–E, 2A–E, and 3A–E, and record your observations in Table 2.

N Use these observations to estimate the $[H_3O^+]$ in the $HC_2H_3O_2$ solution and record your estimate in Table 2.

6. How do the strengths of HCl and the $HC_2H_3O_2$ compare? Explain how this affects their behavior.

_____

_____

_____

_____

_____

More Tubes!

Tube 4: 3.0 mL of 0.1 M $HC_2H_3O_2$, 3 drops of thymol blue

Tube 5: 3.0 mL of 0.1 M $HC_2H_3O_2$, 3 drops of methyl orange

Tube 6: 3.0 mL of 0.1 M $HC_2H_3O_2$, 3 drops of methyl red

○ Using the estimated $[H_3O^+]$, record the pH of the 0.1 M $HC_2H_3O_2$ solution in Table 2.

7. How did you arrive at this estimate?

_____

_____

8. Compare concentrations and pH values of 0.1 M $HC_2H_3O_2$ and 0.001 M HCl. How do they compare? What does this mean?

_____

_____

_____

_____

COMPARING AN UNKNOWN ACID TO STANDARDS

P Label the last three test tubes "7," "8," and "9." Using the 10 mL graduated cylinder, measure 3.0 mL of the unknown weak acid into these test tubes.

Q Add three drops of thymol blue solution to Tube 7, three drops of methyl orange solution to Tube 8, and three drops of methyl red solution to Tube 9.

R Compare the colors in Tubes 7–10 with the appropriate indicator standards in Tubes 1A–E, 2A–E, and 3A–E, and record your observations in Table 2.

S Use these observations to estimate the $[H_3O^+]$ and pH of the unknown weak acid and record your estimate in Table 2.

Let's practice writing some equations and acid-ionization constant expressions for a weak acid, such as hypochlorous acid (HClO). The dissociation equation for dissolving HClO in water is shown below.

$$HClO(aq) + H_2O(l) \longrightarrow H_3O^+(aq) + ClO^-(aq)$$

From this equation we write the K_a expression.

$$K_a = \frac{[ClO^-][H_3O^+]}{[HClO]}$$

A 1.0 M hypochlorous acid solution has a pH of 3.8 because it produces a hydronium ion concentration of 1.73×10^{-4} M. We can therefore conclude two things about the concentrations in the solution. Because the coefficients of the hydronium ions and hypochlorite ions are both one, we know that their concentrations will be equal. Therefore, $[ClO^-] = 1.73 \times 10^{-4}$ M too. We also know that since very little of a weak acid dissociates, we can assume that the concentration of HClO is still 1.0 M. We can substitute these values into the K_a expression to calculate the acid-ionization constant for HClO.

Even More Tubes!

Tube 7: 3.0 mL of 1.0 M unknown acid, 3 drops of thymol blue

Tube 8: 3.0 mL of 1.0 M unknown acid, 3 drops of methyl orange

Tube 9: 3.0 mL of 1.0 M unknown acid, 3 drops of methyl red

$$K_a = \frac{[H_3O^+][ClO^-]}{[HClO]}$$

$$= \frac{(1.73 \times 10^{-4})(1.73 \times 10^{-4})}{(1.0)}$$

$$= 3.0 \times 10^{-8}$$

Now you can use a similar process to analyze the unknown acid. Ask your teacher for the identity of the acid.

9. Write the equilibrium equation for the dissociation of the acid.

_____

10. Using this equation, write the K_a expression.

11. Find the K_a value for this acid in Appendix I of your textbook. Use the K_a value and your estimated $[H_3O^+]$ to determine the amount concentration of the unknown weak acid.

12. Ask your teacher for the amount concentration of the unknown acid. How well were you able to determine the amount concentration?

_____

13. How did the concentrations and pH values of the unknown acid and the 0.1 M acetic acid compare?

_____

_____

_____

Going Further

14. On the basis of what you learned in this lab activity, why do you think buffer systems use a weak acid and its conjugate base?

_____

_____

15. How do you think knowing the strength of an acid would make a difference?

_____

_____

_____

TABLE 2

Test Tubes	Thymol Blue	Methyl Orange	Methyl Red	$[H_3O^+]$	pH
Group A				0.1	
Group B				0.01	
Group C				0.001	
Group D				0.0001	
Group E				0.000 01	
$HC_2H_3O_2$ (4, 5, and 6)					
Unknown Weak Acid (7, 8, and 9)					

QUESTIONS

» What does it mean to standardize a solution?

» How do I do titration?

» How can I determine the concentration of vinegar by titration?

Say Cheese!

Measuring Concentration by Titration

At Shelburne Farms in Vermont, blocks of cheddar cheese are set to age in a cooler. But how do the cheese makers at Shelburne Farms know when the cheese is ready? This is where chemistry comes in. Farmers do a titration of the whey from cheese to determine its acidity. The acid in cheese is lactic acid, which is what helps cheese to develop taste and texture.

How do chemists determine amount concentration of acids and bases?

We can also determine when a particular level of acidity has been reached by using a pH meter or an indicator. In this experiment, you will find the concentration of a vinegar by doing an acid-base titration.

Procedure

Before we can titrate the vinegar, we must first determine the concentration of a standardized solution by titrating it with a primary standard. A *primary standard* is a chemical substance that is easy to work with and of such purity that it can be used as a reference.

SETTING UP

A Add about 100 mL of NaOH solution to a clean, dry 150 mL beaker.

B Observe the burettes set up by your teacher. Burette A is for the acid and Burette B is for the base.

C Check that the tip of Burette B is filled with liquid (no air in the tip). If necessary, drain some of the NaOH solution out of the burette into the waste beaker provided by your teacher. If there is not enough solution, use a funnel to carefully fill Burette B with NaOH solution until the level of the liquid is near but not above 0.00 mL. Record this initial volume of NaOH under Trial 1 in Table 1.

EQUIPMENT

- laboratory balance
- beakers, 150 mL (2)
- ring stand
- burette clamp
- burettes, 50 ml or 100 mL (2)
- funnel
- Erlenmeyer flasks, 250 mL (2)
- wash bottle
- pipette
- sodium hydroxide (NaOH) solution
- potassium hydrogen phthalate ($KHC_8H_4O_4$)
- distilled water
- phenolphthalein solution
- white vinegar
- goggles
- laboratory apron
- nitrile gloves

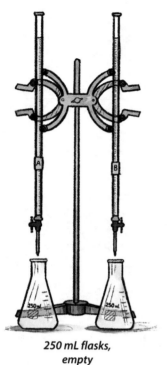

100 mL burette filled with vinegar *100 mL burette filled with 01. M NaOH solution*

250 mL flasks, empty

▲

Acid-base titration setup

1. How are the calibrations of a burette different from that of a graduated cylinder?

_____

_____

_____

D Measure the mass of one of the Erlenmeyer flasks and record this value under Trial 1 in Table 1.

STANDARDIZING THE NaOH SOLUTION

E Add 1.0–1.5 g of potassium hydrogen phthalate (KHP) to the flask on the balance. Measure and record the combined mass under Trial 1 in Table 1.

F Calculate the mass of KHP used. Record this result under Trial 1 in Table 1.

2. Write a balanced chemical equation for the reaction of NaOH with KHP to form water and sodium potassium phthalate.

_____

G Add at least 30 mL of distilled water to the flask and swirl the flask until all the solid dissolves. Wash any crystals that cling to the wall of the flask down into the solution with a few milliliters of water from a wash bottle.

3. Why does the water not need to be measured accurately?

_____

_____

_____

H Add two drops of phenolphthalein indicator to the KHP solution in the flask.

4. The structure of phenolphthalein is shown in the image at right. Phenolphthalein is a white solid. But you are using drops of solution. Suggest what it might be dissolved in. (*Hint*: Think about the polarity of phenolphthalein.)

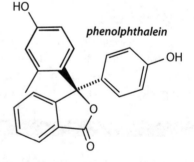

phenolphthalein

_____

_____

I Place the flask on a piece of white paper under Burette B. Lower the burette until the tip extends into the flask.

5. What do you think is the purpose of the white paper?

_____

_____

J Titrate the KHP solution by adding a few milliliters of NaOH solution from Burette B as you swirl the flask to mix the solutions (see image at right). Stop adding NaOH when the light pink color doesn't go away with swirling. Read the final volume on the burette and record it in Table 1.

K Calculate the volume of NaOH used in this trial and record it in Table 1.

L Dispose of the waste in accordance with your teacher's instructions, then rinse out your flask well. Repeat Steps D–J to do Trial 2 for standardizing the NaOH solution.

6. Describe the color change that you observed for phenolphthalein in the trials on the basis of the acidity or basicity of the solution.

_____

_____

7. Calculate the moles of NaOH used in each trial. Show your work for Trial 1 below. Record your answers for both trials in Table 1.

Titrating the unknown solution

8. Calculate the amount concentration of the NaOH for each trial. Show your work for Trial 1 below. Record your answers for both trials in Table 1.

HOW TO TITRATE

1. Control the stopcock with one hand while you swirl the flask with the other hand.

2. Continue to titrate by adding the NaOH solution slowly until the light pink color lingers before disappearing; then add the NaOH by drops.

3. Stop titrating when the light pink color remains for at least 30 seconds; you have reached the end point.

4. If the pink color fades, add one drop at a time until there is a change from colorless to a permanent pink.

M Calculate the average amount concentration on the basis of the values that you calculated for each trial and record this as the amount concentration for NaOH in Table 2 (enter twice).

N Refill Burette B with NaOH solution for the next part of the activity.

O Pour about 55 mL of white vinegar into the second clean, dry 150 mL beaker.

P Check that the tip of Burette A is filled with liquid (no air in the tip). If necessary, drain some of the vinegar solution out of the burette into the appropriate waste beaker provided by your teacher. If there is not enough solution, use a funnel to carefully fill the burette with vinegar solution until the level is near but not above 35.00 mL. Record the initial volume of vinegar in Table 2.

Q Allow about 15 mL of the vinegar to drain into the other clean 250 mL Erlenmeyer flask. Add two drops of phenolphthalein indicator to the vinegar in the flask.

R Record the initial volume of the NaOH in Table 2.

S Titrate the vinegar in the flask with the NaOH solution from Burette B.

T If you feel like you've added more than barely the amount needed to titrate the solution, add a few drops of vinegar from the burette and then carefully add NaOH until one drop causes the color to change to pink. Read the final volumes of the NaOH and vinegar and record both in Table 2.

U Calculate the volumes of NaOH and vinegar used in each trial and record them in Table 2.

9. Write the balanced chemical equation between sodium hydroxide and acetic acid.

V If needed, refill your burettes and repeat Steps O–T to accomplish a second trial.

10. Calculate the moles of acetic acid neutralized in each trial. Show your work for Trial 1 below. Record your answers for both trials in Table 2.

11. Calculate the amount concentration of the vinegar for each trial.
    Show your work for Trial 1 below. Record your answers for both trials in
    Table 2.

12. Report the average amount concentration of acetic acid on the basis of
    the values that you calculated for each trial. Show your work in the mar-
    gin if needed.

    _____

Going Further

13. Use dimensional analysis with the amount concentration, molar mass,
    and density (1.01 g/mL) of acetic acid to calculate the mass fraction of
    acetic acid in your vinegar.

    _____

    _____

14. Check your bottle of vinegar. How does this compare with what the label
    says?

    _____

    Scientists titrate more than just the things you eat, like the lactic acid in
    the whey of cheese. Titration is used during the production of biodiesel fuel,
    for aquarium water testing, and in medical analysis such as medication levels
    in IV drips and the glucose levels of diabetic patients.

15. How do these uses of titration play a role in helping people solve real-
    world problems?

    _____

    _____

    _____

    _____

    _____

TABLE 1

	Trial 1				Trial 2			
	Mass (g)	Volume (mL)	Moles	M (mol/L)	Mass (g)	Volume (mL)	Moles	M (mol/L)
Flask								
Flask and $KHC_3H_4O_4$								
$KHC_3H_4O_4$								
NaOH Initial								
NaOH Final								
NaOH Used								

TABLE 2

	Trial 1			Trial 2		
	Volume (mL)	Moles	M (mol/L)	Volume (mL)	Moles	M (mol/L)
NaOH Initial						
NaOH Final						
NaOH Used						
Vinegar Initial						
Vinegar Final						
Vinegar Used						

19A LAB

QUESTIONS

» How do chemical reactions produce electricity?

» How does the choice of material for electrodes affect a redox reaction?

EQUIPMENT

- digital multimeter
- beaker, 50 mL
- alligator clip leads (2)
- white vinegar (5%, acetic acid)
- mechanical pencil leads (4)
- tape
- sandpaper
- zinc strip or galvanized nail
- magnesium ribbon
- goggles
- laboratory apron
- nitrile gloves

The Dead, Twitching Frog Mystery

Investigating a Voltaic Cell

A whole new world opened to chemists in the late 1790s with the discovery of electrochemistry. When Alessandro Volta built the first battery, he probably didn't realize the significance of his invention. Volta created the battery to settle a dispute that he was having with fellow scientist Luigi Galvani. Galvani had noticed that a freshly dissected frog leg would twitch when he touched it with two strips of different metals joined at one end. He believed that this experiment demonstrated the existence of what he called "animal electricity"—electricity generated by a biological system.

Where does the electricity in a battery come from?

Volta disagreed with Galvani's interpretation of his experiment. Volta believed that the electricity originated because of the dissimilar metals. He constructed a number of simple batteries to confirm that biological material was not needed. In an example of one of Volta's batteries shown below, a battery is made from a series of cups containing an electrolytic solution and strips of two different metals. In reality, both Volta and Galvani were partially correct. Volta was right in that the metals were the key to what Galvani had observed. But Galvani was correct in believing that biological tissues *can* generate electricity. Neither, however, understood the essential role that an electrolyte played in the overall picture.

Let's take a look at Volta's battery to expand our understanding of redox reactions—the chemistry that makes a battery work.

One of Volta's batteries, known as a "crown of cups"

Procedure

SETTING UP

A Fill the beaker with approximately 40 mL of acetic acid.

B Connect the alligator clip leads to the multimeter's probes. Switch the meter on and set it to measure DC voltage.

C Form the mechanical pencil leads into a bundle, using a small piece of tape in the middle to secure them. They will act as a carbon electrode. Gently connect the alligator clip lead coming from the positive (+) multimeter probe (usually red) to one end of the bundle.

TESTING METALS

D Using the sandpaper, rub the zinc strip so that it brightens, and then clip the alligator lead connected to the negative (–) multimeter probe (usually black) to one end of the zinc strip.

1. Why is it important to clean the metal with sandpaper before performing the experiment?

_____

_____

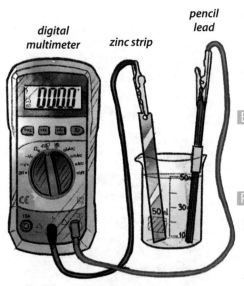

digital multimeter   **zinc strip**   **pencil lead**

E Dip the carbon and zinc electrodes in the acetic acid, making sure that they don't touch. As soon as the multimeter gives a definite voltage reading, record this value in Table 1. Generally, the voltage will start to drop within just a few seconds, so read the meter quickly.

F Repeat Steps D and E using the magnesium strip in place of the zinc.

2. What did you observe around the magnesium strip during the procedure?

_____

_____

3. How could you experimentally determine whether your observations for Question 2 were due to a redox reaction with the carbon or to the magnesium reacting with the acid?

_____

_____

_____

G Use the procedure that you outlined in Question 3 to determine whether the observations in Question 2 were due to a redox reaction. When sanding the magnesium ribbon, lay the ribbon on the table and sand the flat surface. ***The edge of the ribbon can cause significant cuts.***

4. What did you conclude in Step G? Explain.

_____

_____

_____

H Connect the carbon and zinc electrodes with a single alligator clip lead between them (see image at right). The meter will not be used.

I Immerse the two electrodes in the acetic acid, making sure that they don't touch. Leave the setup undisturbed for 10 minutes. Read on and answer Questions 5–12 while you wait.

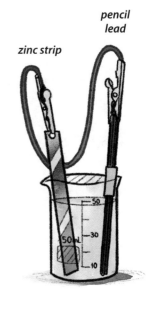

pencil lead

zinc strip

Voltaic cells involve redox reactions, but what is being oxidized and what is being reduced? The following equations describe the reaction for the first experiment (zinc electrode).

$$Zn(s) \longrightarrow Zn^{2+}(aq) + 2e^-$$

$$2H^+(aq) + 2e^- \longrightarrow H_2(g)$$

5. What's happening in the first reaction? How do you know?

_____

_____

_____

The setup for the voltaic cell

6. Where is the zinc going? How do you know?

_____

_____

_____

7. Where are the electrons going? How do you know?

_____

_____

_____

8. What is happening electrically to the zinc electrode?

_____

_____

_____

9. If this process goes on long enough, what do you expect will happen to the zinc electrode?

_____

_____

_____

10. What's happening in the second reaction? How do you know?

_____

_____

_____

11. Where are the hydrogen ions in the second equation coming from?

_____

_____

12. What do you expect to see happening as a consequence of the second reaction?

_____

_____

J After 10 minutes has elapsed, carefully examine both electrodes in a good light. Do not touch or jiggle them!

13. What do you observe?

_____

_____

14. Describe in detail what you think is happening when you connect the electrodes together and immerse them in the acid.

_____

_____

_____

_____

_____

15. Does the carbon electrode undergo a redox reaction? Explain.

_____

_____

_____

_____

16. What role do you think the carbon electrode plays in the voltaic cell?

_____

_____

_____

COMPARING VOLTAGES

When you measured the voltages developed by the zinc and magnesium, you may have wondered why they were different. Volta and other scientists also observed that batteries made from different metals performed differently. Eventually scientists figured out a way to classify different materials to predict how they would behave in a battery.

Each substance to be tested is used as an electrode in a voltaic cell containing a 1 M electrolyte solution at STP (see image below). The second electrode is made from a glass tube containing hydrogen gas. This electrode is treated as a *standard reference electrode*, which is assumed to have a value of 0 V. The voltage between the two electrodes is measured. Since the reference electrode is assumed to be 0, the voltage reading is considered to be the tested material's specific voltage value.

Apparatus used to determine standard electrode potentials

17. Ignoring the sign on the standard electrode potentials for zinc and magnesium given in Table 1, compare those standards to your measured values. Do the measured values reflect the general trend shown by the standard values?

_____

_____

18. Are the measured values reasonably close to the standard values?

_____

_____

19. If they are *not* reasonably close, can you think of possible reasons to account for the difference?

_____

_____

_____

_____

_____

Going Further

20. So where do you think the electricity comes from in a nickel-zinc battery?

_____

_____

_____

21. If zinc and nickel have a voltage of −1.2 V and +0.5 V respectively when testing in the voltaic cell described above in "Comparing Voltages," what voltage would you expect from a nickel-zinc battery?

_____

_____

_____

TABLE 1

Material	Measured Voltage (V)	Standard Electrode Potential (V)
zinc (Zn)		−0.76
magnesium (Mg)		−2.37

19B LAB

Essential Medicine

Using Redox Titration

The World Health Organization (WHO) includes potassium permanganate on its list of essential medicines. As a medicine, it is used to treat a number of skin diseases. It is also used in processes of water purification to remove iron and hydrogen sulfide. It can also combat invasive species such as zebra mussels. These applications all involve redox reactions.

In this lab activity you will do a redox titration to find out the concentration of a potassium permanganate solution ($KMnO_4$). You won't need an indicator for this titration—the potassium permanganate acts as its own indicator! As this redox titration reaches its end point, you will watch the solution change color, similar to the color change of the indicator in acid-base titrations.

How can I use titration for redox reactions?

QUESTIONS

» How can I model the movement of electrons in a redox reaction?

» How is the concentration of an oxidizer determined by titration?

EQUIPMENT

- laboratory balance
- beaker, 150 mL
- burette, 50 mL
- burette clamp
- ring stand
- filtering funnel
- beaker, 50 mL
- weighing dish
- Erlenmeyer flask, 125 mL
- wash bottle with distilled water
- graduated cylinder, 10 mL
- graduated cylinder, 100 mL
- potassium permanganate solution ($KMnO_4$)
- iron(II) sulfate heptahydrate ($FeSO_4 \cdot 7H_2O$)
- distilled water
- sulfuric acid (H_2SO_4), 6 M
- goggles
- laboratory apron
- nitrile gloves

Procedure

SETTING UP

A Add about 60 mL of $KMnO_4$ solution to a clean, dry 150 mL beaker.

1. Record your observations of the $KMnO_4$ solution.

_____

_____

_____

B Make sure that your titration setup looks like the image shown at left. Check that the burette stopcock is closed and, with the aid of a funnel, carefully fill the burette with $KMnO_4$ solution. Open the stopcock and drain out some of the solution into the 50 mL beaker until the tip of the burette is filled. Check that the level of the $KMnO_4$ solution is near but not above 0 mL. Record the starting volume in the Trial 1 column of Table 1.

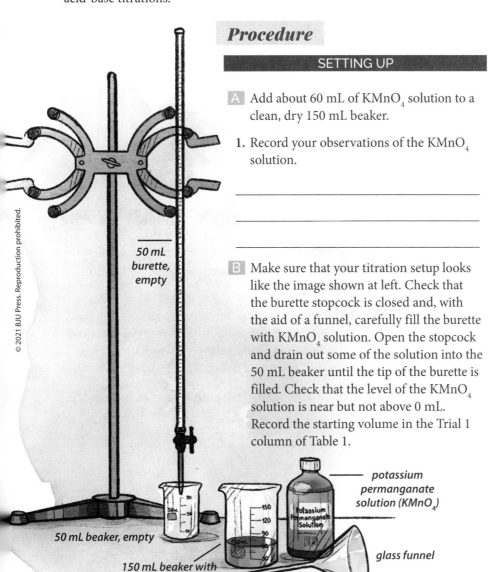

50 mL burette, empty

50 mL beaker, empty

150 mL beaker with 60 mL $KMnO_4$

potassium permanganate solution ($KMnO_4$)

glass funnel

C Using a weighing dish, obtain approximately 0.70 g of iron(II) sulfate ($FeSO_4$). Record the mass of the iron(II) sulfate in Table 1. Transfer the iron(II) sulfate to the flask.

2. Write the chemical equation for the reaction of permanganate ions with iron(II) ions to form manganese and iron(III) ions. Don't be concerned with balancing the elements in this equation for now.

_____

3. Why are the potassium and sulfate ions not included in this reaction?

_____

_____

4. Which element is being reduced? Which is being oxidized?

_____

5. Which element is the reducing agent? Which is the oxidizing agent?

_____

D Add approximately 10 mL of distilled water to the flask and swirl the flask until all the solid iron(II) sulfate dissolves. Use a few milliliters of water from a wash bottle to wash any crystals that cling to the wall of the flask down into the solution.

E Using the 10 mL graduated cylinder, add 1 mL of 6 M sulfuric acid (H_2SO_4) to the flask.

6. What does the sulfuric acid add to the solution that affects the redox reaction?

_____

_____

TITRATING KMnO₄

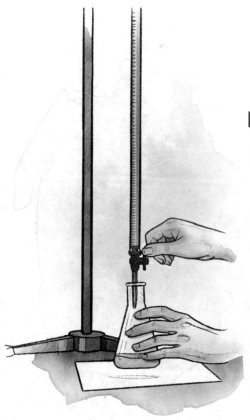

F Place the flask on a piece of white paper under the burette. This will help you see when the color in the flask starts changing. Lower the burette until the tip extends into the flask.

G Titrate the $FeSO_4$ solution by adding a few milliliters of $KMnO_4$ from the burette as you swirl the flask to mix the solutions (see image at left). Stop adding $KMnO_4$ when the light pink color doesn't go away with swirling. Read the final volume in the burette and record it in Trial 1 of Table 1.

H Calculate the amount of $KMnO_4$ used in the titration and record it in Table 1.

I Now do a second trial. Refill the burette with $KMnO_4$ solution and record the initial volume in the Trial 2 column of Table 1.

J Repeat Steps D–H for a second sample of iron(II) sulfate.

K Drain any unreacted potassium permanganate solution from your burette into the waste beaker provided by your teacher.

7. Describe the color change that you observed as you did the titration.

_____

_____

_____

_____

_____

The balanced redox equation for the reaction of potassium permanganate and iron(II) sulfate is shown below.

$$2KMnO_4(aq) + 8H_2SO_4(aq) + 10FeSO_4(aq) \longrightarrow$$
$$K_2SO_4(aq) + 2MnSO_4(aq) + 5Fe_2(SO_4)_3(aq) + 8H_2O(aq)$$

This might make a little more sense if you look at what is happening to the ions.

$$2MnO_4^-(aq) + 16H^+(aq) + 10Fe^{2+}(aq) \longrightarrow$$
$$2Mn^{2+}(aq) + 10Fe^{3+}(aq) + 8H_2O(l)$$

8. What happens to the oxygens in the permanganate ion?

_____

_____

L Calculate the moles of $KMnO_4$ reacted in each titration. Show your work for Trial 1 below and record your answers for both trials in Table 1.

M Calculate the amount concentration of the KMnO$_4$ solution. Show your work for Trial 1 below and record your answers for both trials in Table 1.

N Obtain the expected concentration of the potassium permanganate solution from your teacher and calculate a percent error. Show your work for Trial 1 below and record your answers for both trials in Table 1.

Going Further

9. Potassium permanganate is used for medical purposes such as treating skin diseases and infections. On the basis of what you have observed in this activity, suggest some reasons why.

_____

_____

_____

TABLE 1

	Trial 1	Trial 2
Initial Volume $KMnO_4$ (mL)		
Mass of $FeSO_4$ (g)		
Final Volume $KMnO_4$ (mL)		
Volume $KMnO_4$ used (mL)		
Moles of $KMnO_4$		
Amount Concentration $KMnO_4$ (mol/L)		
Percent Error		

Makes Scents!

Synthesizing Esters

The smell that we associate with bananas is due to a naturally produced ester called *3-methylbutyl acetate*. This ester can be synthesized in laboratories to be used for everything from banana-flavored chewing gum to solvents for varnishes and lacquers. This chemical also has the very convenient ability to attract large numbers of honey bees—an amazing design feature of banana trees!

Where do artificial scents come from?

Smaller esters, such as 3-methylbutyl acetate, have an attractive scent. They form when an alcohol reacts with a carboxylic acid. The hydrogen from the alcohol reacts with the hydroxyl group on the carboxylic acid to form water.

$$R-C{\overset{O}{_{O-H}}} + R'OH \rightleftharpoons R-C{\overset{O}{_{O-R'}}} + H_2O$$

In this lab activity you'll actually get to make some chemicals that smell good! You'll mix three different combinations of carboxylic acids and alcohols to form three different esters.

EQUIPMENT

- microwave oven
- beakers, 50 mL (3)
- test tubes (3)
- test tube rack
- beaker, 250 mL
- laboratory thermometer
- pipettes (3)
- test tube clamp
- distilled water
- 2-hydroxybenzoic acid ($C_7H_6O_3$)
- methanol (CH_3OH)
- ethanoic acid (CH_3COOH)
- ethanol (CH_3CH_2OH)
- propan-2-ol ($CH_3CHOHCH_3$)
- sulfuric acid, concentrated (H_2SO_4)
- sodium bicarbonate ($NaHCO_3$) solution
- labeling tape or grease pencil
- goggles
- laboratory apron
- nitrile gloves

QUESTIONS

» What esters can be formed from different carboxylic acids and alcohols?

» How can I produce an ester?

Procedure

A Label three 50 mL beakers "1," "2," and "3," and fill each half full with distilled water. You will be using these beakers of water to help you observe the smell of the esters that you produce.

B Label three clean, dry test tubes "1," "2," and "3."

1. In the reaction shown on page 199, what do the R and R′ represent?

_____

Later in this activity, you will add sulfuric acid to the mixtures of carboxylic acids and alcohols and then heat these mixtures.

2. Keeping in mind that the reaction is an endothermic process, what do you think is the purpose for heating the reaction and adding the acid?

_____

_____

You will put the following carboxylic acid and alcohol pairs into the test tubes as follows:

Tube 1: 2-hydroxybenzoic acid and methanol

Tube 2: ethanoic acid and ethanol

Tube 3: ethanoic acid and propan-2-ol

3. What is R and R′ for 2-hydroxybenzoic acid and methanol? See the structure of 2-hydroxybenzoic acid below.

4. Write a reaction predicting the result of combining 2-hydroxybenzoic acid and methanol.

_____

[C] Name the ester produced in this reaction, and record it in the Tube 1 row of Table 1.

5. What is R and R′ for ethanoic acid and ethanol?

_____

6. Write a reaction predicting the result of combining ethanoic acid and ethanol.

_____

[D] Name the ester produced in this reaction, and record it in the Tube 2 row of Table 1.

7. What is R and R′ for ethanoic acid and propan-2-ol?

_____

8. Write a reaction predicting the result of combining ethanoic acid and propan-2-ol.

_____

[E] Name the ester produced in this reaction, and record it in the Tube 3 row of Table 1.

Now you're ready to make some esters!

COOKING UP SOME ESTERS

[F] Fill the 250 mL beaker half full with hot tap water. Heat it in a microwave to about 70 °C, *but no warmer*.

[G] In Tube 1, add 10 drops of 2-hydroxybenzoic acid and 20 drops of methanol.

[H] In Tube 2, add 10 drops of ethanoic acid and 20 drops of ethanol.

[I] In Tube 3, add 10 drops of ethanoic acid and 20 drops of propan-2-ol.

[J] Now add 2 drops of concentrated sulfuric acid to each tube. The sulfuric acid acts as a catalyst to help speed up the reaction between the alcohol and the carboxylic acid. Swirl to mix the contents of each tube.

NO FLAMES!

The chemicals you are working with in this activity are highly flammable, so make sure that there are no laboratory burners turned on as you work.

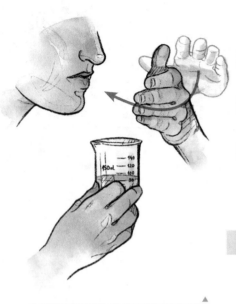

This is how you observe the aroma of the solutions in the beakers.

K Put all three test tubes into the hot water. Let them sit in the water for about five minutes. If the contents of a test tube begin to boil, raise the test tube out of the hot water with a test tube holder, and then return it to the hot water bath when boiling stops.

L Let the test tubes cool. Add 10–20 drops of sodium bicarbonate (NaHCO$_3$) solution, about 1 g, until the contents of the tube stop fizzing.

M Pour the contents of each test tube into the beaker that corresponds to it. Tube 1 gets poured into Beaker 1, for example.

N Waft the aroma of each liquid toward your nose (see left), and describe what you observe in Table 1. You may want to waft the aromas of the carboxylic acids and alcohols to contrast the smells. ***Do not put your nose directly over the containers while smelling.***

Going Further

9. What kinds of products would esters be useful for? Explain.

_____

_____

_____

10. Where would the esters to make these products come from, and how could chemistry help?

_____

_____

_____

_____

_____

TABLE 1

	Carboxylic Acid	Alcohol	Ester	Observations
Tube 1	2-hydroxybenzoic acid	methanol		
Tube 2	ethanoic acid	ethanol		
Tube 3	ethanoic acid	propan-2-ol		

Name _____

Date _____

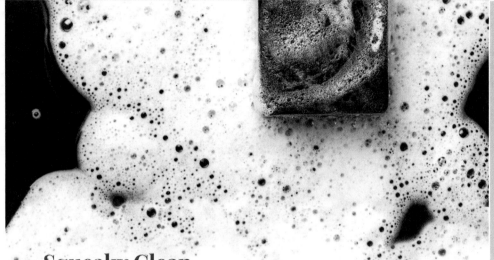

Squeaky Clean

Investigating Soaps and Detergents

The soap-making process has been known for over 2000 years. Prior to AD 100, soap was used as a medicine, but since that time it has been used primarily for washing and cleaning. Early soap makers produced soap by the same process that is still used today. During this process, called *saponification*, a metal hydroxide is heated with a lipid to produce a fatty acid salt and glycerol (together called soap). Originally, the potash (potassium compounds, e.g., KOH) in wood and plant ashes provided the hydroxide for the reaction; today NaOH is used. The following reaction shows this saponification process.

How do soaps and detergents work?

EQUIPMENT

- laboratory balance
- graduated cylinder, 100 mL
- beaker, 250 mL
- weighing dish (2)
- stirring rod
- test tubes (6)
- test tube brush
- test tube rack
- graduated cylinder, 10 mL
- spatula
- corks (6)
- metric ruler
- beaker, 50 mL
- ring stand with iron ring
- filtering funnel
- filter paper
- distilled water
- magnesium sulfate heptahydrate ($MgSO_4 \cdot 7H_2O$)
- bar of soap
- liquid detergent
- shampoo
- cooking oil
- trisodium phosphate (Na_3PO_4)
- goggles
- laboratory apron
- nitrile gloves

$$CH_2-O-C(=O)-(CH_2)_{16}-CH_3$$
$$CH_2-O-C(=O)-(CH_2)_{16}-CH_3 \; + \; 3 \, NaOH \longrightarrow \begin{matrix} CH_2-OH \\ CH-OH \\ CH-OH \end{matrix} \; + \; 3 \, CH_3-(CH_2)_{16}-C(=O)(O-Na^+)$$
$$CH_2-O-C(=O)-(CH_2)_{16}-CH_3$$

a fat   +   metal hydroxide → glycerol   +   fatty acid

When dissolved in water, soap can remove grease and dirt from surfaces as a result of its structure. A soap molecule has a nonpolar end that dissolves in oil or grease, and it has a polar end that dissolves in water. As the soap molecules dissolve in the oil or grease, the polar ends remain protruding from the droplet that forms. Thus, the soap forms a coating on the oil or grease that appears negatively charged to water molecules and results in clusters known as *micelles*. Once coated, the oil or grease is said to be *emulsified*. It can then mix with water and be rinsed away. In this lab activity, you will conduct a series of three tests to investigate how soaps and detergents work.

QUESTIONS

» How do soaps and detergents act in hard water?

» Is soap, detergent, or shampoo better at removing oils?

» How can I soften hard water?

Procedure

HARD WATER TEST

Hard water is water that contains a significant amount of dissolved minerals. The solubility and cleaning action of soap are greatly reduced in hard water due to the presence of calcium and magnesium ions, which form insoluble carboxylates with the soap. For this reason, soap is often replaced by a synthetic detergent, which has a structure and a function similar to soap but does not form the insoluble compounds in hard water that soap does.

While the presence of suds is not a requirement for soap or detergent to clean well, the loss of suds may indicate the loss of cleansing power.

1. What ion is responsible for creating the hard water in this lab activity?

_____

A. Using a 100 mL graduated cylinder, measure 150 mL of distilled water and place it in the 250 mL beaker. Using the weighing dish and laboratory balance, measure 3.0 g $MgSO_4 \cdot 7H_2O$, then mix it with distilled water. Stir well. This will be your hard water stock solution.

B. Clean three test tubes, and drain as much water from them as possible. Label the tubes "1," "2," and "3," then place them in the test tube rack.

C. Use the 10 mL graduated cylinder to add 10 mL of distilled water to Tube 1, 10 mL of tap water to Tube 2, and 10 mL of the prepared hard water stock solution to Tube 3.

D. Using a spatula, add a dime-sized scraping of bar soap to each of the test tubes.

E. Cork the test tubes and shake each one individually up and down vigorously ten times. Return each tube to the rack and wait one minute. Then use the metric ruler to measure the height of the suds in each tube. (Wherever you are asked in this lab activity to measure the suds, consistently measure only the suds that span the tube, not where they are thin and consist of only a few bubbles.) Record your measurements in Table 1.

F. Dispose of the contents of the three test tubes. Clean the tubes thoroughly with the brush, rinse them with tap water, and then do a final rinse with distilled water.

2. Why do you think the bar soap produced the different suds heights in the different samples of water?

_____

_____

_____

_____

_____

G. Repeat Steps C through F, but substitute 10 drops of liquid detergent for the bar soap.

H. Repeat Steps C through F again, but substitute 10 drops of shampoo for the bar soap.

3. Which cleanser produced the most suds in each type of water?

_____

4. Why does a detergent form suds in hard water when soap doesn't?

_____

_____

_____

_____

EMULSIFYING ACTION TEST

I. Clean a fourth test tube, label it "4," and allow it to drain. Place it with the other three test tubes in the test tube rack. Add 10 mL of the prepared hard water stock solution to Tubes 1–4.

J. Add 20 drops of cooking oil to each test tube.

K. Using your spatula, add a nickel-sized scraping of bar soap to Tube 2. Add 20 drops of liquid detergent to Tube 3 and 20 drops of shampoo to Tube 4.

5. What is the purpose of Tube 1?

_____

_____

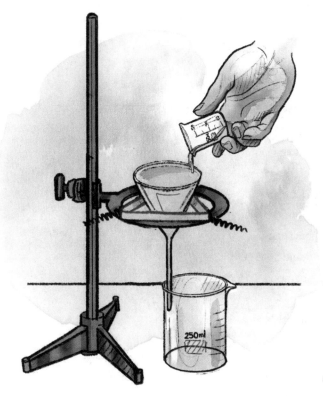

L Cork the tubes and individually shake each test tube vigorously up and down twenty times. Return each tube to the rack and wait ten minutes. While waiting, continue on to Steps N and O in the Precipitation Test below. After ten minutes, use the metric ruler to measure the height of the suds in each test tube and record your measurements in Table 1.

M Since the goal of removing grease or oil is to emulsify it, or break it up and suspend it in the water, you should also note whether there is a difference in the amount of visible oil droplets at the surface, just under the suds. If the oily layer is not obvious or is milky, you have evidence that it has been emulsified.

6. How did each cleanser perform in the emulsification action test?

_____

_____

_____

_____

7. Which substance is the best emulsifying agent in hard water: soap, detergent, or shampoo? Explain your reasoning.

_____

_____

_____

_____

_____

PRECIPITATION TEST

Commercial laundry and dishwasher detergents also contain substances that soften the water and thus aid their cleaning ability. In this part of the activity, we will use trisodium phosphate to soften the water.

8. Write the balanced equation for the reaction of magnesium sulfate with trisodium phosphate.

_____

N Using the weighing dish and laboratory balance, measure 2.0 g Na_3PO_4, then mix it with 20 mL of the hard water stock solution in the 50 mL beaker.

O Stir a couple of minutes, or until all the Na_3PO_4 is dissolved. Note that since a precipitate is forming as the Na_3PO_4 dissolves, it may be difficult to determine when the Na_3PO_4 is completely dissolved.

P Set up the filtration equipment as shown at right. Filter the white precipitate. Dispose of the filtered precipitate in accordance with your teacher's instructions and save the clear filtrate.

Q Clean the last two test tubes, label them "5" and "6," and allow them to drain. Place them in the test tube rack. Add 10 mL of the clear filtrate to Tube 5 and 10 mL of stock hard water solution to Tube 6.

R Add a dime-sized scraping of bar soap to each of the tubes.

S Cork the tubes and shake them ten times. After one minute, use the metric ruler to measure the height of the suds in each tube. Record your measurements in Table 1.

9. According to your data, do you think shampoo is more like a detergent or a soap? Explain your reasoning.

_____

_____

10. Did Na_3PO_4 affect the hardness of the water? What is the basis for your answer?

_____

_____

_____

_____

Going Further

11. One of the key defenses against many diseases (flu, coronavirus, and other viruses) is hand washing. Why do you think that emphasis is put on using soap and washing for at least twenty seconds?

_____

_____

_____

_____

TABLE 1

Hard Water Test		
Water	**Cleanser**	**Suds (cm)**
distilled	bar soap	
tap		
hard		
distilled	liquid detergent	
tap		
hard		
distilled	shampoo	
tap		
hard		
Emulsifying Action Test		
Cleanser	**Suds (cm)**	
none		
bar soap		
liquid detergent		
shampoo		
Precipitation Test		
Additive	**Suds (cm)**	
none		
Na_3PO_4		

Name _____

Date _____

Balancing Act

Testing Macronutrients in Food

What should I have for lunch? This is a question that most people ask each day. We like to think about what we enjoy eating and what tastes good, but we should also think about what macronutrients are in our food. All the energy we need comes from the food we eat. While we don't need to eat a completely balanced meal every time, we should seek to understand the sources of the building blocks that we need and the foods that provide them to us.

Am I eating balanced meals?

In this lab activity you will test the ingredients of a common sandwich to see which macronutrients are in each ingredient. We will test for the presence of carbohydrates (both starches and sugars), proteins, and lipids (fats).

Procedure

A balanced meal should include carbohydrates, proteins, and lipids. The appropriate proportions of these depend on the energy needs of the individual, but the general rule of thumb is that we need 15%–35% of our calories to come from proteins, 25%–35% from lipids, and 35%–65% from carbohydrates.

EQUIPMENT

- laboratory balance
- labeling tape or grease pencil
- beakers, 50 mL (7)
- disposable pipettes (7)
- test tubes (5)
- test tube rack
- rubber stoppers (10)
- graduated cylinder, 10 mL
- mortar and pestle
- weighing dishes (3)
- vegetable oil, 10 mL
- egg white, 10 mL
- cornstarch solution, 10 mL
- glucose solution, 10 mL
- distilled water, 10 mL
- biuret solution, 20 mL
- iodine solution, 20 mL
- brown lunch bag
- glucose test strips (8)
- food for testing
- goggles
- laboratory apron
- nitrile gloves

QUESTIONS

» What is a balanced meal?

» What macronutrients do the components of a sandwich provide?

» What can I add to my lunch to make it more balanced?

To begin, you will test five substances to determine your baseline data for positive and negative results for each macronutrient—lipid, protein, and carbohydrate (both starch and sugar). You will test vegetable oil, egg whites, cornstarch solution, glucose solution, and water.

A Label five beakers from 1 to 5.

B Pour 10 mL of each of the following samples into the labeled beakers as follows—vegetable oil (1), egg white (2), cornstarch solution (3), glucose solution (4), and water (5).

1. Identify the macronutrient for which each solution will provide the positive control indication.

_____

_____

C Label two additional beakers "Biuret Solution" and "Iodine Solution."

D Pour 20 mL of the appropriate solution in these two labeled beakers.

Biuret solution contains sodium hydroxide (NaOH), which is a strong base. Bases are corrosive and must be handled with care. If you spill any biuret solution on your skin, wash immediately and notify your teacher. Iodine is less hazardous, but it will stain your skin and clothes.

E Place a pipette in each of the seven beakers.

You will test for lipids by putting some of each sample on a brown paper bag.

F Cut the brown lunch bag so that you have a single layer of paper. Section your brown paper bag into six sections and label five of them from 1 to 5 corresponding to the solutions in Beakers 1–5. Save the sixth section for the Testing Lunch Food portion of this activity.

G In each section, rub the bag with some of the appropriate liquid. Wipe off any excess sample without spreading it into other sections.

H Allow the material on the paper to dry, about 10–15 minutes. (While you wait, continue with the Protein Test below.)

I Once the bag is dry, hold the bag up to a bright light. Record in the Lipid Test column of Table 1 whether the bag in each test area is opaque or translucent.

J After collecting your data, set the bag aside until Step DD.

2. What is the indication of a positive test for lipids according to your observations?

_____

PROTEIN TEST

The usual test for the presence of a protein in food is the biuret test. In this test, a liquid sample is mixed with biuret solution. A color change takes place if peptides are present.

K Label five test tubes from 1 to 5 corresponding to the solutions in Beakers 1–5.

L Using the pipettes, transfer 3 mL each from Beakers 1–5 to the appropriate test tubes.

M Using a pipette, add 3 mL of biuret solution to each of the test tubes. Stopper the tubes, shake well, and let sit.

N Allow time for a color change to occur—about 3–5 minutes. Record your observations in the Protein Test column of Table 1.

3. What are the indications of positive and negative results for proteins according to your observations?

_____

_____

O Empty the test tubes into the waste collection beaker provided by your teacher. Rinse and dry the test tubes for use in the Starch Test.

STARCH TEST

Iodine solution is used to test for the presence of starch in foods.

P Label five test tubes from 1 to 5 corresponding to the solutions in Beakers 1–5.

Q Using the pipettes, transfer 3 mL each of Beakers 1–5 to the appropriate test tubes.

R Using a pipette, add 3 mL of iodine solution to each of the test tubes. Stopper the tubes, shake well, and let sit.

S After a couple of minutes, observe any color change. Record the color in the Starch Test column of Table 1.

4. What are the indications of positive and negative results for starches according to your observations?

_____

_____

T Empty the test tubes down the drain with excess water. Rinse and dry the test tubes.

A glucose test strip is used to test for the presence of sugar in foods.

U Divide a piece of paper into five sections and label them from 1 to 5 corresponding to the solutions in Beakers 1–5. Place a glucose test strip in each section.

V Take each test strip from its section, dip it in the appropriate sample, and return it to the paper.

W After three minutes, use the color code provided with the test strips to evaluate each strip and record the results in Table 1.

5. What color indicates the presence of glucose?

_____

X After you have collected your data, dispose of the test strips and paper in the trash.

Y Dispose of any unused sample materials down the drain with excess water. Then clean and dry Beakers 1–5 for use in the next section. You also still need the biuret and iodine solutions, so don't dispose of them.

6. Why did we test the water?

_____

_____

Now that you know the process for testing each of the macromolecules, it's time to test some food. Select three ingredients of a typical sandwich, perhaps your favorite! You will now test each of these ingredients for the four different macromolecules.

Z Label three of the beakers appropriately for the foods that you will be testing.

AA Using the laboratory balance and a weighing dish, obtain an approximately 2 g sample of the first food item for testing. Since the food samples are solid, you need to crush each sample with a mortar and pestle. Once sufficiently crushed, transfer the sample to one of the beakers.

BB Using the 10 mL graduated cylinder, add 10 mL of water to the beaker and stir.

CC Repeat Steps AA and BB for each sandwich ingredient. Be sure to clean the mortar and pestle between foods.

DD Repeat the macromolecule tests on each ingredient and record your data in Table 2.

EE When finished, dispose of all biuret solution (used and unused) in the disposal container. Dispose of all other liquids down the drain with excess water. Dispose of all solids in the trash.

7. Which ingredients contained proteins? starches? sugars? lipids?

_____

_____

Going Further

8. Did your lunch contain a balance of macronutrients?

_____

_____

9. If your meal was not balanced, what food would be a good choice to make it balanced?

_____

_____

_____

TABLE 1 *Test Control Data*

Test Tube	Material	Positive for	Lipid Test	Protein Test	Starch Test	Glucose Test
1	vegetable oil	lipid				
2	egg whites	protein				
3	corn starch solution	starch				
4	glucose solution	glucose				
5	water	none				

TABLE 2 *Lunch Data*

Item	Lipids		Protein		Carbohydrates			
					Starch		Glucose	
	Translucent?	Present?	Color	Present?	Color	Present?	Color	Present?

Name _____

Date _____

The Proof Is in the Jell-O

Investigating Enzymes

Enzymes are polymers of amino acids that act as catalysts in nearly every biochemical reaction in living organisms. They regulate the speed of a reaction by providing an alternative reaction mechanism with a lower activation energy. Like all catalysts, they are not consumed by the reaction. The amino acid sequence and the three-dimensional structure of the enzyme molecule determine how specific the action of an enzyme will be. It is thought that the various folds of the amino acid chains bring certain areas of the chain together in the same region, forming pockets, or active sites, into which only a specific substrate will fit.

How do enzymes affect biochemical reactions?

Enzymes are required for most biochemical reactions to proceed at an organism's core temperature. Without them, large quantities of reactants, extremely high temperatures, and long intervals of time would be required for reactions to occur. Several factors affect the activity of an enzyme, including temperature, pH, inhibitors, and activators, all of which are specific for particular enzymes. For example, most human enzymes exhibit optimum activity between 35 °C and 40 °C, but the bacteria that inhabit hot springs have enzyme systems that can effectively operate at 70 °C or higher.

Bromelain is an enzyme found in pineapple. It is classified in the group of enzymes called *proteases*—enzymes that separate proteins into amino acids. Gelatin is a protein from animal bones and connective tissues. In its pure form, gelatin is colorless, odorless, tasteless, brittle, and transparent. Although you may be more familiar with gelatin as a dessert dish, its uses are far broader than the production of food. Gelatin is also used in the manufacture of photographic film, in bacteriology as culture media, and in medicine as capsule shells and surgical dressings.

QUESTIONS

» How do enzymes affect gelatin?

» How does temperature affect the activity of an enzyme?

» Which foods contain enzymes that affect gelatin the most?

EQUIPMENT

- microwave oven
- freezer
- beakers, 50 mL (11)
- beaker, 600 mL
- labeling tape or grease pencil
- prepared gelatin
- pineapple, fresh, canned, and frozen (but thawed)
- apple
- banana
- fig
- grape
- kiwi
- papaya
- goggles
- laboratory apron

In this lab activity, you will determine the effect of the enzyme bromelain on gelatin and the effect of temperature on the activity of this enzyme. Then you will determine whether other fruits affect gelatin in a manner similar to the way that pineapple does.

1. Why would the necessary conditions for biochemical reactions without enzymes, as described in the introduction, be a problem for living organisms?

_____

_____

_____

_____

Procedure

TESTING ENZYMES

A Label the 50 mL beakers from 1 to 11.

B Obtain a sample of prepared gelatin from your teacher and divide it equally between the beakers.

C Microwave a sample of fresh pineapple for 1 minute on high. Set it aside to cool.

2. Hypothesize about what effect you think heating pineapple will have on the activity of the enzyme bromelain.

_____

_____

Once you have placed fruit samples as described in the steps below, you will observe each fruit's effect on gelatin after 10 minutes, 20 minutes, and 30 minutes. Therefore, you will want to get all your samples prepared in advance so that you can place them on the gelatin at approximately the same time.

D Place a sample of fresh pineapple on the surface of the gelatin in Beaker 2.

E Once the pineapple from Step C has cooled, place it on the surface of the gelatin in Beaker 3.

F Place a sample of the thawed pineapple on the surface of the gelatin in Beaker 4.

G Dry any excess juice from a sample of canned pineapple and then place the pineapple on the surface of the gelatin in Beaker 5.

H After 10, 20, and 30 minutes, examine the sample in each beaker and record your observations in Table 1.

TESTING OTHER FRUIT

☐ Place a sample of the following fruits into the labeled beakers as follows: fresh apple (6), banana (7), fig (8), grape (9), kiwi (10), and papaya (11).

☐ After 10, 20, and 30 minutes, examine the sample in each beaker and record your observations in Table 2.

3. What do you think you are testing with the samples of pineapple that are heated and frozen? What effect do you think heating and freezing will have on the enzyme? Explain.

_____

_____

_____

_____

4. What is the purpose of Beaker 1?

_____

_____

5. Which sample(s) of pineapple did *not* dissolve the gelatin?

_____

6. Which sample(s) of pineapple caused the gelatin to dissolve?

_____

7. How are the canned and the microwaved samples similar?

_____

_____

8. What conclusion can you draw about the effect of freezing on this particular enzyme?

_____

_____

9. Are the effects on the bromelain that you determined experimentally different from your predictions in Question 2?

_____

_____

10. Of the fruits that you tested, which one(s) dissolved the gelatin? What does this observation indicate?

_____

_____

11. Have you ever made Jell-O salad? You have to be careful about which fruit you put in your salad! Explain which fruits will and will not work.

_____

_____

Going Further

12. Exocrine pancreatic insufficiency (EPI) is a condition in which the pancreas fails to produce key digestive enzymes. What would you expect might be some symptoms of EPI?

_____

_____

_____

13. What would you expect for common treatments of EPI?

_____

_____

_____

TABLE 1

	Beaker 1	Beaker 2	Beaker 3	Beaker 4	Beaker 5
	No Pineapple	Fresh Pineapple	Microwaved Pineapple	Thawed Pineapple	Canned Pineapple
10 min					
20 min					
30 min					

TABLE 2

	Beaker 6	Beaker 7	Beaker 8	Beaker 9	Beaker 10	Beaker 11
	Apple	Banana	Fig	Grape	Kiwi	Papaya
10 min						
20 min						
30 min						

22A LAB

Name _____

Date _____

It's Only a Matter of Time

Investigating Half-Life

The word *radioactive* makes many people nervous. They associate radio-activity with the negative aspects of this fascinating field of chemistry. In reality, our discovery of radioactivity has led to many benefits for people.

There are many uses for radioactivity in a variety of fields. If you walk through a hospital, you can find many applications that use nuclear chemistry. In addition to the obvious x-rays, there are other imaging applications, such as CT scans and PET scans. You can find radioac-tivity being used in the form of radiotracers in nuclear pharmacology.

How can I model radioactive decay?

Nuclear chemistry is used to provide food and water around the world. A large portion of our produce is irradiated to destroy bacteria and insects. Nuclear chemistry is also applied in the desalination of water. Even everyday items such as watches, clocks, and smoke detectors operate using radioactive isotopes.

While there are many benefits of nuclear radiation, there are also haz-ards. As with many technologies, we have to take advantage of the beneficial aspects while minimizing the negative aspects. For example, how long will a material remain radioactive? How do we store it while it remains radioactive? In this lab activity, you will investigate radioactive decay and decay series.

1. What is radioactive decay?

_____

_____

2. What is half-life?

_____

_____

QUESTIONS

» What determines how long a sample will remain radioactive?

» How is the decay model affected if the decay products are also radioactive?

EQUIPMENT

• three different color paper "isotopes" (red, white, and blue; 100 each)

3. You have a sample that contains 137.6 g of copper-64. Copper-64 is unstable and has a half-life of 12.70 h. It undergoes beta decay to become stable zinc-64. After 1.75 d, how much of your sample will still be copper-64 and how much will be zinc-64?

Procedure

SIMPLE DECAY

In these simple decay trials we are assuming that each of our radioactive isotopes undergoes a single decay event to become a stable atom.

A Start with 40 paper "isotopes," which are blank on one side and have an X on the other.

4. What do you think each paper represents?

_____

5. What do you think the two different sides of the paper represent?

_____

_____

B Predict how many of the atoms you expect to decay during a first drop of the papers. Record your prediction in Table 1.

6. What does each drop of the papers represent?

_____

C Drop the papers onto the table or floor from at least 1 m up. All subsequent drops should also be made from at least 1 m up.

D Separate all the decayed atoms—the ones with the marked side facing up—from the undecayed. Count the number of decayed atoms, record this value in Table 1, and then set these decayed atoms aside.

E Count the number of undecayed atoms and record this value in Table 1.

F Using only the undecayed atoms, repeat Steps B–E until all the atoms are decayed.

G Repeat Steps A–F for two more trials.

7. What effect would adding more papers have on the number of drops needed to decay all the papers?

_____

_____

_____

H Repeat Steps B–G, starting with 60 papers. Record the data from these trials in Table 2.

8. Were there challenges to making predictions? Explain. How did you solve any challenges? Why did you choose any solutions that you used?

_____

_____

_____

_____

9. Were your predictions correct for all the numbers of decayed atoms?

_____

10. Could you have made better predictions? Explain.

_____

_____

11. Were the numbers of half-lives exactly the same each trial? Why or why not?

_____

_____

12. On average, how many additional half-lives were required to decay the 60 atom samples versus the 40 atom samples? Does this make sense? Explain.

_____

_____

_____

_____

13. On the basis of your results, how much time would it take for 60 atoms of radium-226 ($t_{1/2}$ = 1599 y) to decay?

14. Using the data from Trials 4–6, compare the average numbers of atoms that decayed during the first half-life to the average number that decayed in the fifth half-life. Do these results make sense? Explain.

_____

_____

_____

_____

[I] Create a scatterplot of undecayed atoms in Trials 1–3 on a single graph. Make each trial its own color. Create a second scatterplot of undecayed atoms in Trials 4–6. Make each trial its own color.

15. How do the trends of the two scatterplots compare? What type of mathematical relationship do the scatterplots represent?

_____

_____

DECAY SERIES

In the second part of this lab activity we will model a decay series in which each original atom has to go through three decay events before it is stable.

[J] Start with 100 red papers.

[K] Drop the papers onto the table.

[L] Count all the undecayed red atoms and record this value in Table 3.

[M] Count all the decayed atoms and replace each decayed red paper with a white paper. Record the number of white papers in Table 3.

[N] Drop the papers onto the table again.

[O] Separate all the decayed atoms from the undecayed. Replace the decayed red papers with white papers. Replace the decayed white papers with blue papers.

[P] Record how many red, white, and blue papers you now have in Table 3.

[Q] Drop the papers onto the table again.

[R] Separate all the decayed atoms from the undecayed. Replace the decayed red papers with white papers. Replace the decayed white papers with blue papers. Remove the decayed blue papers.

[S] Record how many red, white, and blue papers you now have.

[T] Repeat Steps Q–S until all the blue papers are removed.

16. How do you expect a scatterplot of the decay series will compare with the first two scatterplots?

_____

_____

_____

_____

[U] Create a scatterplot of undecayed atoms in the decay series on a third graph. Each color will be its own curve.

17. How did the decay series differ from the simple decay? Was this as you expected?

_____

_____

_____

_____

Going Further

18. Many radioactive isotopes need a multistep decay series before they become a stable isotope. What does what you observed in this lab activity imply about the issue of nuclear waste?

_____

_____

_____

_____

_____

19. Does your answer to Question 18 imply that we should abandon the use of nuclear materials?

_____

_____

_____

_____

_____

20. From your study of biology, you may recall a concept called *genetic drift*, which describes how the frequency of gene variants within a population of organisms, called *allele frequency*, changes over time. Do an internet search using the keywords "genetic drift." Then compare genetic drift and nuclear decay as examples of random processes.

_____

_____

_____

_____

_____

_____

_____

TABLE 1 *Simple Decay*

Half-Life	Trial 1			Trial 2			Trial 3		
	Predicted Decayed	Total Decayed	Undecayed (remaining)	Predicted Decayed	Total Decayed	Undecayed (remaining)	Predicted Decayed	Total Decayed	Undecayed (remaining)
0			40			40			40
1									
2									
3									
4									
5									
6									
7									

TABLE 2 *Simple Decay*

Half-Life	Trial 4			Trial 5			Trial 6		
	Predicted Decayed	Total Decayed	Undecayed (remaining)	Predicted Decayed	Total Decayed	Undecayed (remaining)	Predicted Decayed	Total Decayed	Undecayed (remaining)
0			60			60			60
1									
2									
3									
4									
5									
6									
7									
8									

TABLE 3 *Decay Series*

Half-Life	Red Papers Remaining	White Papers Remaining	Blue Papers Remaining	Blue Papers Removed
0	100	0	0	0
1				
2				
3				
4				
5				
6				
7				
8				
9				
10				
11				
12				
13				
14				
15				
16				

Atomic Asteroids

Determining Mass Defect and Binding Energy

There are some asteroids that are essentially collections of rocks held together by the force of gravity alone. What would it take to break these asteroids apart, especially if one was on a collision course with Earth? The energy required would need to overcome the force of gravity.

Nuclides are like those asteroids in some ways. They are collections of subatomic particles held together by nuclear binding energy. Just like the asteroids, it would take enough energy to overcome the binding energy for nuclides to undergo fission.

A fundamental idea of modern nuclear chemistry is that mass and energy are equivalent. Mass can be changed into energy, and energy can be changed into mass. The equivalence of mass and energy seems to be responsible for the force that holds a nucleus together. The equation $E = mc^2$ relates the quantities of mass and energy. In nuclear reactions, E is nuclear binding energy, m is the mass defect, and c is the speed of light. When a nuclear reaction occurs, a small amount of mass is converted into a large amount of energy.

In this lab activity you will calculate the binding energy per nuclear particle for He-4, Fe-56, and U-232 nuclides so that you can do a direct comparison of the energy packed into these nuclides. You will need to make several preliminary calculations for each atom. You might be surprised to know which nuclides are the most stable!

Where does the mass lost in a nuclear reaction go?

QUESTIONS

» How do I determine mass defect?

» How much energy holds nucleons together in a nucleus?

» How much energy is released in a nuclear reaction?

EQUIPMENT

• reference source (with precise masses of nuclides) or access to the internet

Procedure

You will start the activity by finding the total mass of all the electrons, protons, and neutrons for He-4, Fe-56, and U-232. You will then add these masses together to find the total expected mass of nucleons for each nuclide. Assume that a proton is 1.0073 u, a neutron is 1.0087 u, and an electron is 0.000 55 u. You will then determine the mass defect—the difference between the expected mass and the actual mass of the nuclide. Once you know the mass defect, you can use the mass-energy equation to calculate the binding energy of the nuclide. You can then calculate the binding energy per nucleon (see the graph on page 542 of your textbook). Let's see how this is done by working through these calculations for sodium-23.

Na-23 nuclides have 11 protons, 11 electrons, and 12 neutrons. Use the calculations below as a sample. Make sure that you follow the rules for significant digits.

SAMPLE CALCULATION (Na-23)

Total Mass of Particles:

$$11 \text{ protons}\left(\frac{1.0073 \text{ u}}{\text{proton}}\right) = 11.0803 \text{ u}$$

$$12 \text{ neutrons}\left(\frac{1.0087 \text{ u}}{\text{neutron}}\right) = 12.1044 \text{ u}$$

$$11 \text{ electrons}\left(\frac{0.000 55 \text{ u}}{\text{electron}}\right) = 0.006 05 \text{ u}$$

Total = 23.190 $\underline{7}$5 u

Mass Defect:
For the Na-23 atom, the mass defect is the difference between the total mass of nucleons and the nuclide's actual mass.

$$23.190 \underline{7}5 \text{ u} - 22.989 77 \text{ u} = 0.200 \underline{9}8 \text{ u}$$

$$1 \text{ u} = 1.66 \times 10^{-27} \text{ kg}$$

The mass defect of the Na-23 atom is

$$0.200 98 \text{ u}\left(\frac{1.66 \times 10^{-27} \text{ kg}}{1 \text{ u}}\right) = 3.33\underline{6} 268 \times 10^{-28} \text{ kg}.$$

Binding Energy:
$$E = mc^2$$
$$= (3.33\underline{6} 268 4 \times 10^{-28} \text{ kg})(3.00 \times 10^8 \text{ m/s})^2$$
$$= 3.00\underline{2} 641 2 \times 10^{-11} \text{ J}$$

Binding Energy per Nucleon:
The Na-23 atom has 23 nucleons, so its binding energy per nucleon is

$$\frac{3.00\underline{2} 641 2 \times 10^{-11} \text{ J}}{23 \text{ nucleons}}, \text{ or } 1.305 \times 10^{-12} \text{ J/nucleon.}$$

DATA COLLECTION

A Find the total mass of all the protons, neutrons, and electrons for the three nuclides in Table 1. Show your work for He-4 below. Record the total masses in Table 1.

1. How do these masses compare to the atomic masses on the periodic table? Explain.

_____

_____

_____

B Use reference books or the internet to look up the actual masses of the nuclides. Be aware that these are different from the atomic masses on the periodic table. Record these in Table 1.

C Find the mass defect of each isotope. Convert the mass defect to kilograms. Show your work for He-4 below. Record the mass defects in Table 1.

2. Which nuclide of the three that you worked with in this exercise had the greatest mass defect? Which had the least?

_____

D Calculate the binding energy for each nuclide. Show your work for He-4 below. Record the binding energies in Table 1.

3. Which nuclide had the greatest binding energy? Which had the least?

_____

4. Do your answers to Questions 2 and 3 make sense?

_____

_____

_____

E Calculate the binding energy per nucleon. Show your work for He-4 below. Record the binding energies per nucleon in Table 1.

5. Which atom had the greatest binding energy per nucleon? Which had the least?

_____

6. Do your answers to Questions 3 and 5 make sense?

_____

_____

_____

F Create a scatterplot of the four binding energies per nucleon plotted with mass numbers. Connect them with a smooth curve.

7. Describe any general observations that you have about your graph.

_____

_____

_____

8. Using your curve, estimate the mass number with the highest binding energy per nucleon.

_____

_____

9. Compare your graph with the graph on page 542 of your textbook. What do you notice?

_____

_____

10. If a nuclide were broken apart into its component particles, would the process release or absorb energy? Why?

_____

_____

_____

_____

_____

Going Further

11. A 20-megaton hydrogen bomb releases energy equivalent to that of the explosion of 20 million tons of TNT, a powerful chemical explosive. Use the fact that 1 ton of TNT releases 4.184×10^9 J of energy to calculate how much matter is converted into energy in the explosion.

12. Would it be wrong to use a 20 megaton hydrogen bomb during war? Why or why not?

_____

_____

_____

_____

_____

TABLE 1

	Na-23	He-4	Fe-56	U-232
Mass of Particles (u)	23.1908			
Mass of Nuclide (u)	22.9898			
Mass Defect (u)	0.2010			
Mass Defect (kg)	3.336×10^{-28}			
Binding Energy (J)	3.003×10^{-11}			
Binding Energy per Nucleon (J/nucleon)	1.305×10^{-12}			

Appendix A

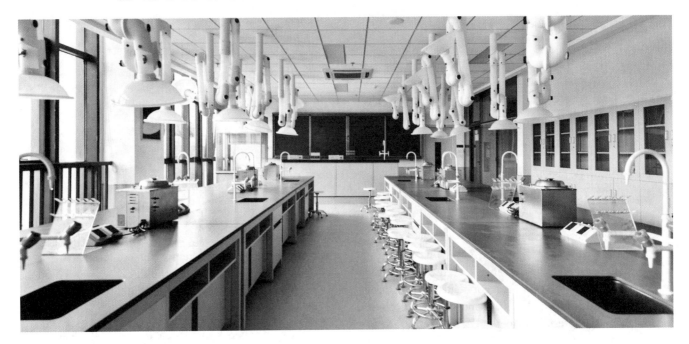

Laboratory Rules

1. Never perform an unauthorized experiment or change any assigned experiment without your teacher's permission.

2. Avoid playful, distracting, or boisterous behavior.

3. Never work alone. Students must not conduct lab activities without supervision.

4. Work at your own lab station.

5. Always work in a well-ventilated area. Use the fume hood when working with toxic vapors. Never put your head in the vent hood.

6. Always wear safety goggles when working with chemicals, glassware, projectiles, and other materials or objects that are potentially hazardous to the eyes.

7. Wear protective clothing and gloves when working with corrosive or staining chemicals.

8. While working in the laboratory, tie back long hair and avoid wearing loose clothing such as scarves or ties.

9. Never taste any chemical, eat or drink out of laboratory glassware, or eat or drink in the laboratory.

10. Always use the appropriate instruments for cutting and handle them carefully. Always cut away from yourself.

11. Thoroughly wash your hands with soap after handling any chemicals.

12. To smell a substance, gently fan its vapor toward you.

13. Never leave a flame or heat source unattended. Keep combustible materials away from heat sources.

14. When diluting acid solutions, always add the acid to water slowly. ***Never add water to an acid!***

15. When heating a test tube, point the open end away from you and others. ***Never heat a closed or stoppered container!***

16. Dispose of waste as instructed by your teacher.

17. Do not return unused chemicals to a container. Dispose of them properly.

18. Notify the teacher of any injuries, spills, or breakages.

19. Know the locations of the fire extinguisher, safety shower, eyewash station, fire blanket, first-aid kit, and Safety Data Sheets (SDS).

Appendix A
LABORATORY SAFETY AND FIRST AID RULES

Basic First Aid

Burns

Flush the area with cold water for several minutes. Do not apply ice.

Chemical Spills

Notify your teacher of all chemical spills.

ON A LABORATORY DESK

- If the material is not particularly volatile, toxic, or flammable, your teacher may have you clean the spill. For liquids, use an absorbent material that will soak up the chemical. For solids, use the designated dustpan and brush. Dispose of chemicals and cleaning materials properly. Then clean the area with soap and water.

- If the material is volatile, toxic, or flammable, and not a large spill, ask your teacher for help. If it is a large spill, you may need to evacuate the laboratory.

- If a highly reactive material, such as hydrochloric acid, is spilled, your teacher will clean it up.

ON A PERSON

- If the spill covers a large area, begin rinsing in the chemical shower, then remove all contaminated clothing and remain under the safety shower. Flood the affected body area for 15 minutes. Obtain medical help immediately.

- If the spill covers a small area, immediately flush the affected area with cold water for several minutes. Then clean the area with soap and water. Get medical attention.

- If the chemical splashes in your eyes, immediately wash them in the nearest eyewash fountain for at least 15–20 minutes. Get medical attention.

- If the spill is an acid, rinse the area with sodium bicarbonate or sodium carbonate solution; if it is a base, use citric or ascorbic acid solution.

Fire

- For any fire other than a contained fire, do *not* attempt to put it out on your own. *Understand that some fires can't be put out with water.*

- Smother a small fire in a container by covering it.

- If a person's clothes are on fire, remember to stop, drop, and roll—roll the person on the floor and use a fire blanket to extinguish the flames. The safety shower may also be used. ***Do not use a fire extinguisher.***

Swallowed Chemicals

Determine the specific substance ingested and follow the instructions on the SDS. Contact the Poison Control Center in your area immediately.

Cuts

If the wound is superficial, clean it with a disinfectant, apply triple antibiotic ointment, and cover with a bandage. If it is a deep cut, seek immediate medical attention.

Appendix B
LABORATORY EQUIPMENT

1. beaker
2. laboratory burner
3. burette
4. burette clamp
5. clay triangle
6. crucible tongs
7. crucible and cover
8. disposable pipette
9. Erlenmeyer flask
10. evaporating dish
11. filter funnel
12. filter paper

1
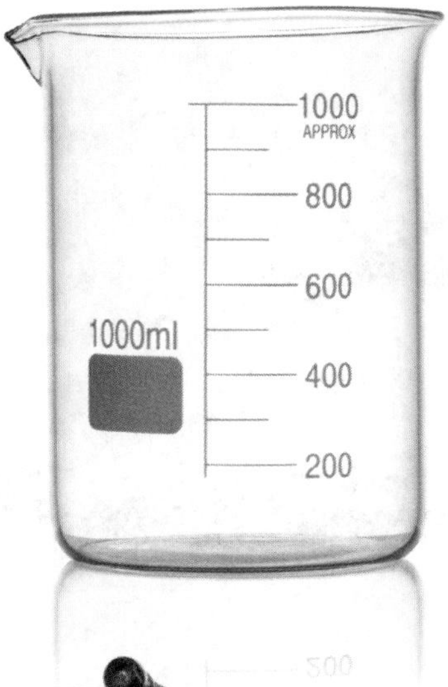

2
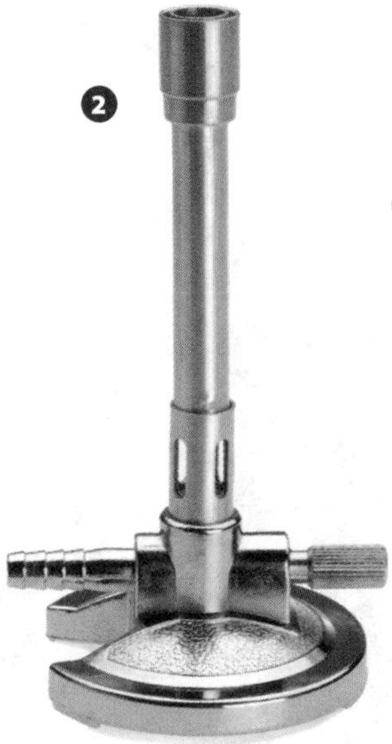

3
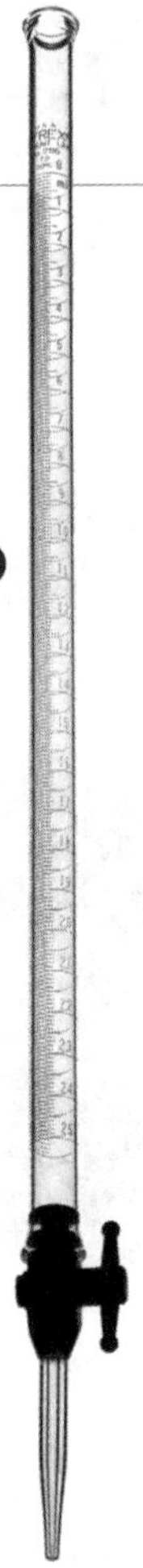

4
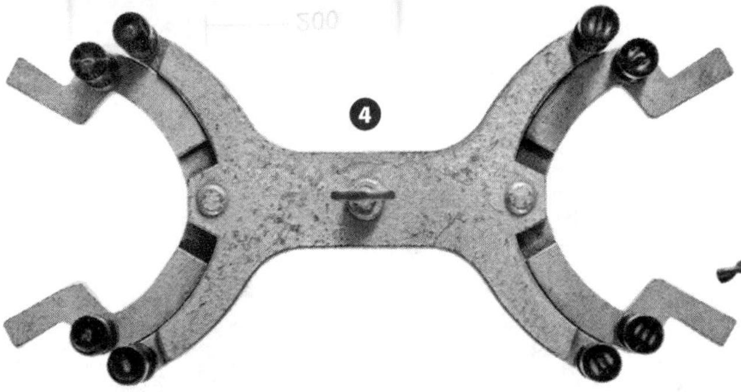

5
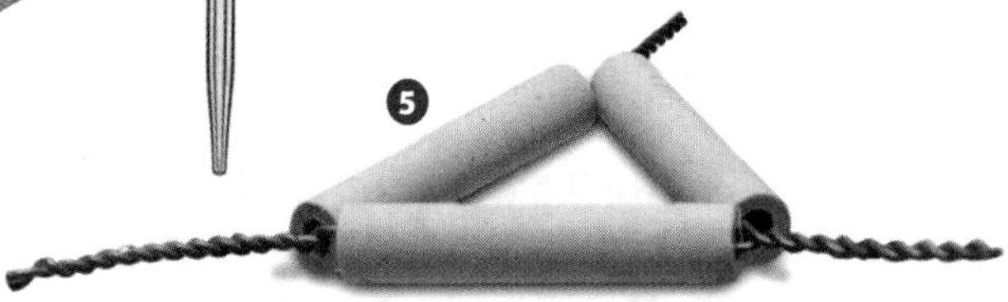

6
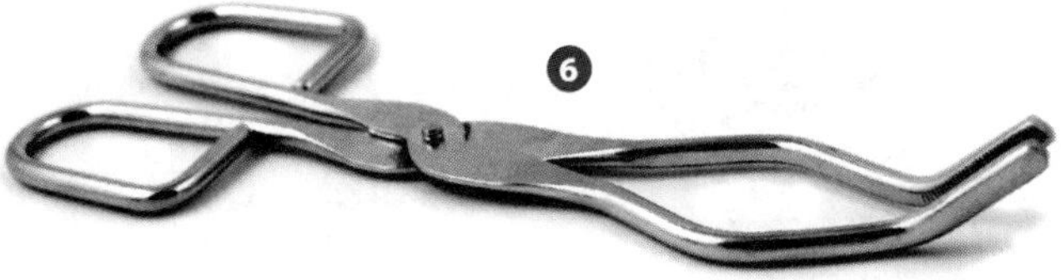

7
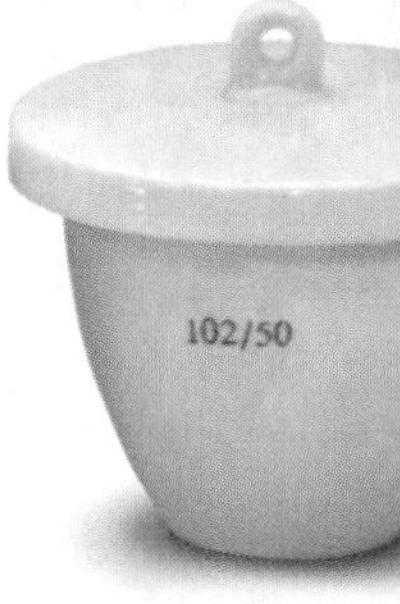

8
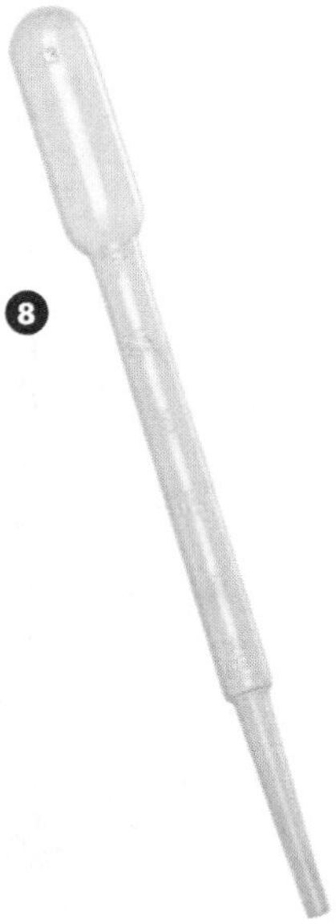

9
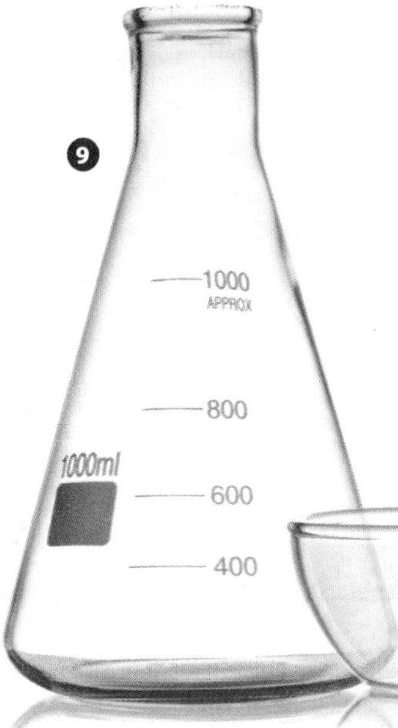

10
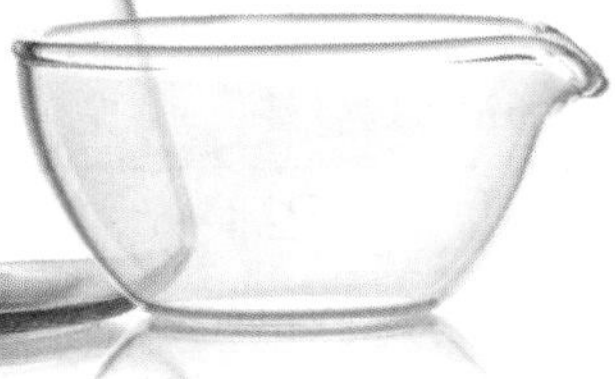

11
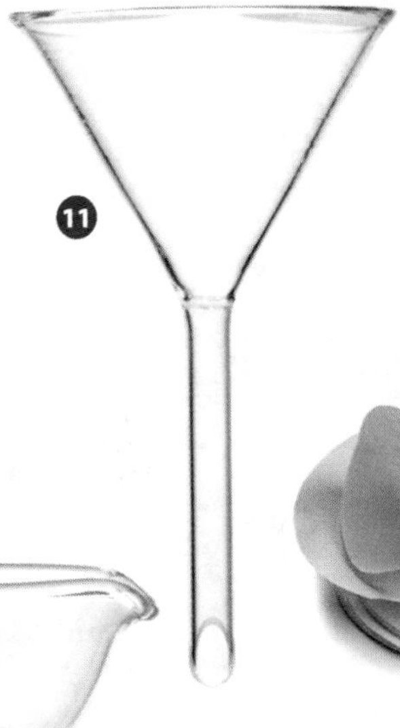

12
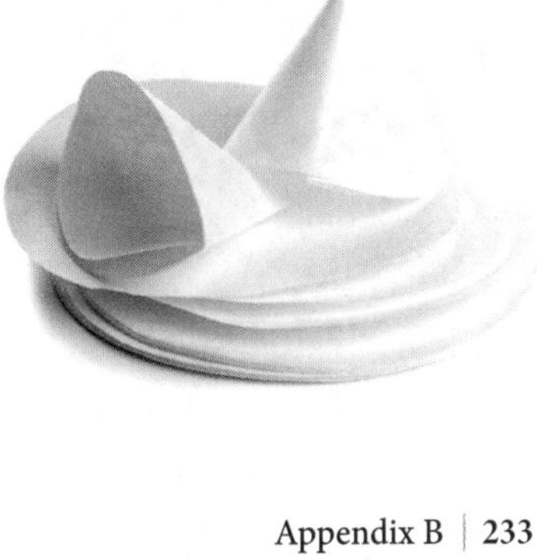

Appendix B

LABORATORY EQUIPMENT

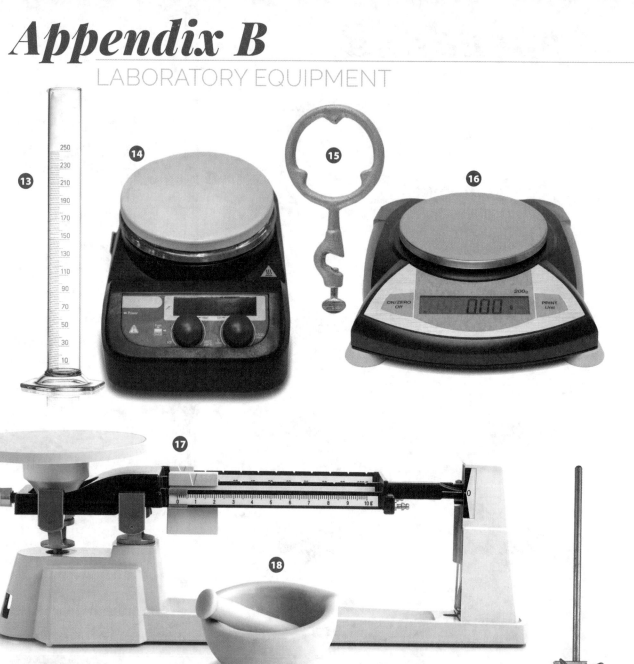

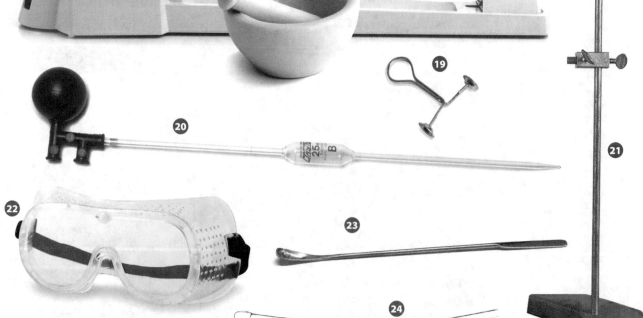

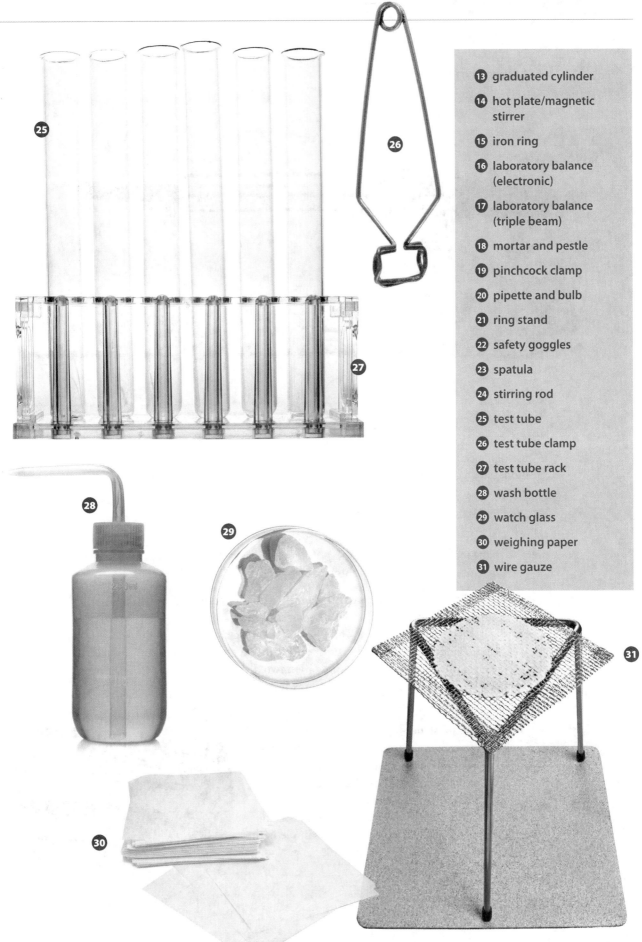

13 graduated cylinder

14 hot plate/magnetic stirrer

15 iron ring

16 laboratory balance (electronic)

17 laboratory balance (triple beam)

18 mortar and pestle

19 pinchcock clamp

20 pipette and bulb

21 ring stand

22 safety goggles

23 spatula

24 stirring rod

25 test tube

26 test tube clamp

27 test tube rack

28 wash bottle

29 watch glass

30 weighing paper

31 wire gauze

Appendix C
LABORATORY TECHNIQUES

Measuring Mass

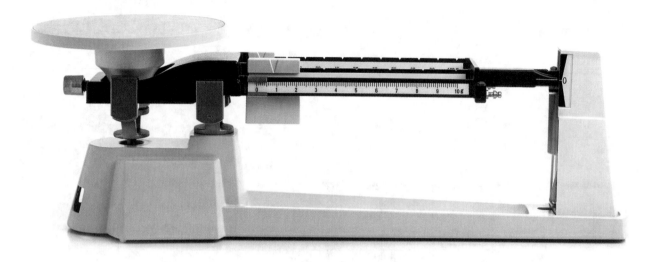

Using Mechanical Balances

The mass of a substance can be determined in the laboratory with the use of a mechanical balance. Several kinds of mechanical balances are common, but all of them operate on the same principles. To use a mechanical balance properly, follow the steps given below.

1. Place the balance on a smooth, level surface.

2. Keep the balance pan(s) clean and dry. Never put chemicals directly on the metal surface of the pan(s). When massing chemicals, place substances on a sheet of weighing paper, watch glass, or in a beaker.

3. Check the rest point of the empty balance. To do this, remove all masses from the pans and slide all movable masses to their zero positions. If the balance beam swings back and forth, note the central point of the swing. You do not have to wait until the beam stops swinging completely. If the central point lies more than two divisions from the marked zero point, ask your teacher to adjust the balance. *Do not adjust the balance yourself!*

4. Place the substance to be massed on the pan and adjust the sliding masses. Move the largest masses first, and then make final adjustments with the smaller masses. If the beam has *detents* for the sliding masses, make sure that the masses rest in the detent. The sum of all the readings is the mass of the object. The mass of the sample in the image at right would be read as 101.43 g.

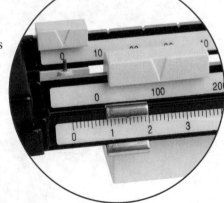

Using an Electronic Balance

Electronic balances are generally faster and easier to use than their mechanical counterparts. To use an electronic balance properly, follow the instructions given below.

1. Place the balance on a smooth, level surface.

2. Keep the balance pan(s) clean and dry. Never put chemicals directly on the metal surface of the pan(s). When massing chemicals, place substances on a sheet of weighing paper, on a watch glass, or in a beaker.

3. Turn the balance on. Place the container or weighing paper that will hold the substance to be massed on the scale and make sure that there is a reading of 0 by pushing the **Tare** button.

4. Place the substance on the container or weighing paper. Add the desired substance until you have reached the appropriate mass.

Using a Laboratory Burner

Laboratory burners are a common source of heat in laboratories. They are popular because they give a hot flame and burn clean, readily available natural gas or butane. Laboratory burners work well because they mix gas with the correct amount of air to produce the most heat. If air is not mixed with the gas before it burns, not all the gas will burn, and the flame will not be as hot. If too much air is mixed with the gas, the air will extinguish the flame.

If the burner doesn't have its own gas supply, connect it to the desk gas line with a rubber hose. Open the main gas valve and light the burner with a match or burner lighter. Adjustments to the flame should be made with the needle valve and air valve (labeled in the image shown at right).

If the burner lights but the flame immediately goes out, try increasing the gas flow at the needle valve. A yellow flame signifies that insufficient air is mixing with the gas. A flame that makes a noise like a roaring wind means that too much air is entering the barrel. This extra air may cool the flame or extinguish it entirely. To get the best flame possible, rotate the barrel until the flame is entirely blue and two distinct zones appear. Place objects to be heated at the tip of the inner blue zone for quick heating. Sometimes the flame strikes back; that is, it enters the barrel and comes out the bottom. If this happens, do not panic. Turn off the gas supply and readjust the burner so that less air enters the barrel.

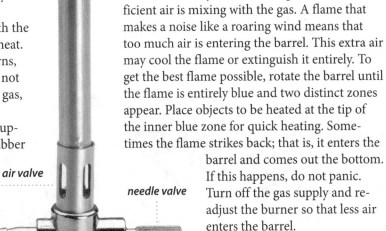

air valve

needle valve

Appendix C
LABORATORY TECHNIQUES

Measuring Chemicals

Proper technique for handling liquids is essential if you are to remain safe, keep reagents pure, and obtain accurate measurements. For increased safety, do not splash or splatter liquids when pouring. Pour them slowly down the insides of test tubes, graduated cylinders, and beakers. If anything is spilled, wipe it up promptly. To keep liquids from running down the outside of the container from which you are pouring, pour the liquid down a stirring rod.

In order to keep the liquid chemicals pure, keep stirring rods out of the stock supply. Do not let the stoppers and lids become contaminated while you are pouring. Instead, hold the stopper between your fingers. If you must put a lid down, keep the inside surface from touching the surface of the laboratory table as shown in the image at right.

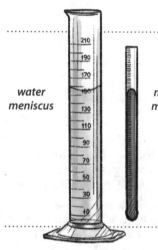

water meniscus

mercury meniscus

Accurate measurements of liquids can be made in burettes, graduated cylinders, and volumetric flasks. You should always measure volumes in these pieces of glassware unless you need only a rough approximation. If the liquid surface curves downward, look at the bottom of the curved surface—the *meniscus* (see left). In some cases the meniscus will curve upward; if that is the case, you should read the volume at its highest point.

To measure out solids, ❶ scoop out a little of the sample onto weighing paper with a spatula, ❷ gently tap the spatula until the desired amount falls off, and ❸ cup the paper to pour the sample into a test tube.

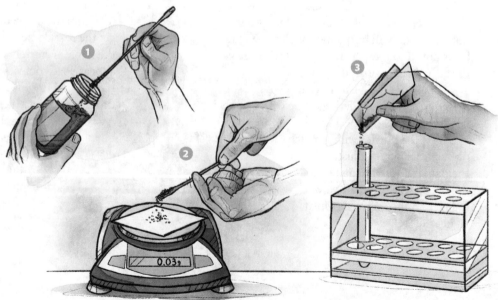

Using a Thermometer

When using a thermometer in lab activities, make sure that you are using one that has the proper temperature range for the experiment that you will be doing. Always hold a thermometer when it is in a container. *Never leave a thermometer standing upright in a container—the container is likely to get knocked over.*

When taking a reading, position the thermometer bulb just above the bottom of the container. If the bulb touches the container, your readings will be inaccurate.

If a thermometer breaks, alert your teacher and do not touch the inner contents. Some thermometers contain mercury. The spilled mercury may look fascinating, but it is toxic and can be absorbed through the skin.

Separating Liquids and Solids

Several experiments require that you separate a solid from a liquid. The most common method of separation—filtering—involves passing the solution through a fine sieve, such as filter paper. The paper allows the liquid and dissolved particles to pass through but catches undissolved particles.

The filter paper must be folded to fit the funnel. Fold it in half and then tear off the corner as shown below. Fold it again at an angle slightly less than 90° to

the first fold. Open the paper to form a cone—half of the cone should have three layers of paper, and the other half should have one. Place the cone in a funnel and wet the paper with a few drops of distilled water to hold it in place. Seal the edge of the paper against the edge of the funnel so that none of the solution can go down the spout without going through the paper.

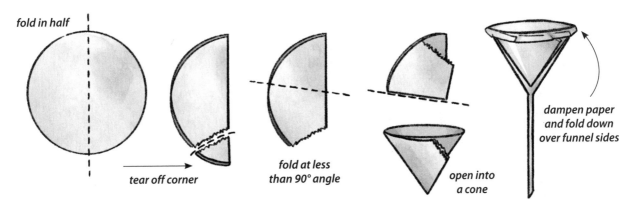

fold in half

tear off corner

fold at less than 90° angle

open into a cone

dampen paper and fold down over funnel sides

Decanting is a quick method that is often acceptable for separating a liquid from a solid. To decant, allow the solid to settle and then gently pour the liquid off the top of the residue (see left). Avoid causing turbulence that could mix the solid with the liquid. Sometimes the solid residue left in the container is rinsed off with distilled water and decanted a second time to make sure that all the liquid is separated from the precipitate.

Appendix D

Constructing Graphs

When data is recorded in tables, it is difficult to see the relationship that exists between sets of numbers. To make trends and patterns easier to see, you will often put your data on a graph.

In experiments that search for a cause-effect relationship between two variables, you will cause one variable (the independent variable) to change and observe the effect on the second (the dependent variable). If you were to investigate how the solubility of NH_4Cl changes with temperature, temperature would be the independent variable and solubility would be the dependent variable. Traditionally, the independent variable is plotted on the x-axis of the graph, and the dependent variable is plotted on the y-axis.

As you construct your graph, choose an appropriate scale. Don't make the graph so small that the data cannot be clearly seen or so large that the graph will not fit on a single sheet of paper. Pick a scale that will conveniently include the entire range of each variable. Keep in mind that the scales on each axis do not have to be the same. For instance, the scale on the x-axis might be 5 °C for every division, while the scale on the y-axis could be 2 g for every division. Your scale should be easy to subdivide. Subdivisions of 1, 2, 5, and 10 are the most convenient.

Once you have decided which variable will be plotted on which axis and the scales that will be used, neatly label the name of each quantity and the numbers on each axis. The title of the graph should be printed at the top of the graph. If more than one line will be sketched on the same graph, include a legend that identifies each line. Plot each of your data points by making small dots. Follow the specific lab guidelines for the proper way to handle these data points. You will usually draw a smooth line through the data points (see below).

TABLE 1

Observed Solubilities of NH_4Cl

Temperature (°C)	Solubility (g/100 mL H_2O)
10	33
20	37
30	41
40	45
50	50
60	56

Solubility of NH_4Cl. Notice how all the points are connected.

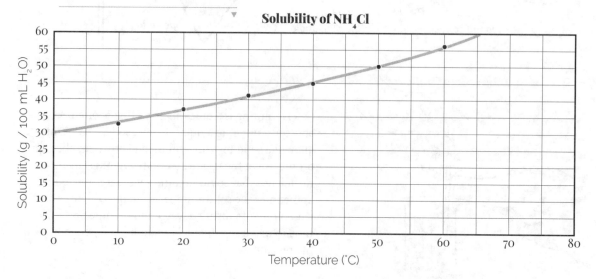

Solubility of NH_4Cl

In some cases, you will want to draw a straight line even though your data points do not fall precisely in a line. If this occurs, draw a line that shows the general relationship. Be sure to make the line go through the average values of the plotted points. In the graph (below, left), line A is incorrect because it lies above the cluster of points near the bottom of the graph and below the cluster of points at the top. Line B (below, right) shows the correct method of fitting a straight line to a series of points.

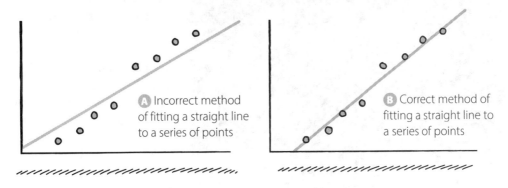

A Incorrect method of fitting a straight line to a series of points

B Correct method of fitting a straight line to a series of points

Interpreting Graphs

The shape of a graphed line tells much about the relationship between the variables. When data appears to be arranged in a straight line, the x and y variables are related in a way that can be expressed in a linear equation. A positive slope means that the y variable increases with the x variable; a negative slope indicates that the y variable decreases as the x variable increases.

Data points that curve up or down from left to right indicate that data may be best modeled by some nonlinear function. Common functions in science include quadratic, exponential, logarithmic, and inverse functions.

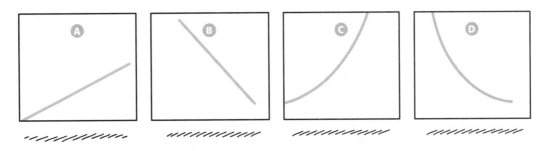

Graphs can be used to predict additional data points that have not been experimentally determined. Assuming that points between verified data points are correct because they fall on the graphed line is called *interpolation*. From the graph of NH_4Cl solubilities on the previous page, it is reasonable to assume that 43 g of NH_4Cl would dissolve at 35 °C. Extending the graphed line past the verified data points in either direction is called *extrapolation*. The graph of NH_4Cl solubilities indicates that 59 g would dissolve at 65 °C. This extrapolation is reasonable, but it may not be totally accurate.

The graphs in this lab manual can have different shapes, including linear relationships (A and B), exponential relationships (C), and inverse relationships (D).

Appendix E

describes how the investigation was conducted, and summarizes what was learned during the investigation. Many college science courses require students to present all their laboratory work in formal lab reports.

To better prepare you for college, your teacher may choose to have you submit your lab assignments in formal lab reports rather than use the fill-in-the-blank format found in your lab manual. You may be more familiar with the latter form, but there is really little to be afraid of about writing formal reports. They may be new to you, and the word "formal" may sound alarming, but with practice such reporting can become second nature.

There really isn't a standardized way of writing and compiling a formal lab report. Your teacher may require you to do all your reporting in a bound journal, or you may be asked to submit individual typed reports. Regardless of which method your teacher prefers, there are some properties of lab reports that teachers generally agree upon. Let's look at the style and mechanics of a formal lab report and the type of content that is normally included.

As you have learned in your study of science, communication is an important part of the scientific process. Part of what scientists do is share what they have learned with other scientists. One example of this is the writing of formal lab reports. In a lab report, a scientist presents a problem that was investigated,

Style and Mechanics

The first thing to keep in mind about a formal lab report is that it is a type of *formal writing*. That means that a formal lab report is like the final draft of an essay or research paper. It should have a neat, orderly appearance. To that end, formal lab reports normally have the following elements of style and mechanics.

- Unbound lab reports should be typed in black ink. Reports in a journal should be *neatly* written.

- Lab reports should be written in complete sentences and be checked for proper spelling, punctuation, and grammar.

- Formal lab reports should be free of erasures, whiteout, or scratched-out words.

- Since objectivity is a key aspect of the scientific process, lab reports usually avoid first-person narrative and instead use an impersonal third-person form.

Example:

DON'T SAY: "I learned that 10 mL of *A* will neutralize 5 mL of *B*." (less formal)

DO SAY: "The results indicated that 10 mL of *A* will neutralize 5 mL of *B*." (more formal)

Format

Scientists (and science teachers) may disagree on the exact number of components in a formal lab report, but there is a general consensus on what is presented and the order in which it is presented. Keep in mind as you write that a formal lab report answers three basic questions.

- What problem was investigated?

- What procedure was used during the investigation?

- What was learned from the investigation?

To answer those questions, a formal lab report generally includes the following elements:

- title

- synopsis

- introduction

- list of any materials used and a description of the procedure

- data yielded by the procedure

- analysis of the data and a discussion of the findings

- sources

Let's take a closer look at each of these.

Title

A formal lab report title should succinctly describe what the lab activity was about. It should be matter-of-fact rather than creative. Consider the following possible titles for a titration experiment.

Example:

INFORMAL: Drip, Drip, Drip!

FORMAL: Comparing the Strengths of Acids Using Titration

It's OK for a formal lab report title to sound dry—save the creative writing for your language arts class! Imagine yourself as another scientist who is reading your report as part of her research; she wants to know right away what your report is about without having to read deep into the main body of the text.

Appendix E

Synopsis

A synopsis is a very brief summary of the entire lab report, that is, two or three sentences. If the title of your report catches the reader's attention, the synopsis should then give the reader just enough detail for him to decide whether he wants to read further.

Example (based on a titration lab):

The suitability of titration using an aqueous solution of sodium hydroxide (NaOH) for distinguishing between acids of different strengths was tested. The results confirmed the ability of sodium hydroxide solution to distinguish between different acids on the basis of a direct relationship between the amount of sodium hydroxide required to neutralize an acid and the number of hydronium ions produced by the acid in an aqueous solution.

Introduction

Your introduction should expand on your synopsis by giving more details about the experiment. An introduction should include the following elements.

- a description of the purpose of the experiment

- the hypothesis that will be tested

- a summary of the methods that will be used to test the hypothesis (Be brief. A more detailed description should be reserved for the Materials and Methods section that follows.)

- a brief description of the results of the procedure

- a summary of the conclusions that you have drawn on the basis of the results

Materials and Methods

The goal of this section of your lab report is to describe your investigation in enough detail to allow another person to assess its validity or even replicate it. That is why there are two parts to this section: materials *and* methods. You should first list your *materials*, including names and quantities where appropriate (e.g., for chemicals). Your list should be just that—a list. Think about how you normally see such lists in a student lab manual.

Next, describe your *methods*. You do not need to give instructions for how to do common laboratory tasks, such as using an electronic balance. Nor do you need to explain how to do common laboratory procedures if your audience is expected to be familiar with them. For example, in the titration example used above it would not be necessary to explain how a titration is done; your audience probably already knows how to do this. What your audience *would* need to know in order to replicate your experiment is the chemicals that you used along with how much and in what concentration. As you write this section, ask yourself whether someone reading your descriptions would be able to replicate your experiment exactly. If the answer is no, then you need to be more specific. It is often helpful to include a diagram of any experimental setup used.

Data

Your data section should be reserved for raw data only. This is where you report the results of your tests. Your data may be *qualitative* (i.e., based on observations) or quantitative (i.e., based on measurements). Often, a good way to report quantitative data is to use a data table. The format of data tables will vary depending on the data that you collected. An excellent technique, especially if you are using spreadsheets, is to record the units of measure in the column header and record only numerical data in the cells. This also allows you to use the computational features of the software. All quantitative data should be reported with the appropriate number of significant figures to indicate the precision of the measurements.

Analysis and Discussion

This is where the fun part begins! Now you get to interpret the data that you presented in the previous section. First, describe how the data was analyzed and show any formulas or equations that were used to do so. Sample calculations should be included. Calculated values should be reported with the proper number of significant figures. Descriptions of the results should include appropriate statistical parameters, such as the mean, median, and range of values. Where appropriate, use graphs to show trends in the data. All graphs should be properly scaled and include titles and axes labels with units.

Once you have presented the analysis of your data, you may then address the all-important question: What does it mean? Think back to your stated hypothesis—did your data and analysis support your hypothesis? Were your results in line with what you expected? How did your results compare with those of others in your class? Be sure to support any claims you make with the relevant data and analyses. Your reader—your teacher —expects to see logical arguments that are consistent with your experimental results.

Your discussion needs to be frank and honest. Don't try to make your data say something that it isn't actually saying. If your data does not support your hypothesis, then say so! Don't say that it does just because you think that might be the answer that your teacher is expecting. An important aspect of nurturing science skills is learning how to discuss inconclusive or contrary data. Examine what may have gone wrong during the experiment, make suggestions for improving future investigations, or propose a modified hypothesis for future testing.

It is also appropriate during your discussion to suggest possible practical applications of your work or to put forward additional related questions that might be investigated in the future. In doing so, you might be laying the groundwork for a future scientist. By this you can see how the process of science has links both to those who have investigated a question in the past and to those who may investigate it in the future.

Sources Cited

Much like any formal research paper, a lab report should cite sources within the body of the report and include a bibliography at the end. There are different formats for doing this. Your teacher will advise you on what format to use.

Photo Credits

Key: (t) top; (c) center; (b) bottom; (l) left; (r) right; (bg) background

COVER
Nick Poon/Moment/Getty Images

FRONT MATTER
i real444/iStock/Getty Images Plus/Getty Images; **ii** game-over/Alamy Stock Photo; **v** agencyby/iStock/Getty Images; **vi–vii**l Portra/Digital Vision/Getty Images; **vii**r ilbusca /Digital Vision Vectors/Getty Images; **viii**t Rat0007/iStock /Getty Images; **viii**b Erik Isakson/Getty Images; **ix** (goggles) Liudmyla Liudmyla/iStock/Getty Images; **ix** (flask) serezniy /iStock/Getty Images

CHAPTER 1
1 Anjelika Gretskaia/Moment/Getty Images; **2** Eskay Lim /EyeEm/Getty Images; **3** whitemay/Digital Vision Vectors /Getty Images; **5** David Tadevosian/Shutterstock.com; **6** JohnnyGreig/E+/Getty Images; **7**l Migrenart/iStock/Getty Images Plus/Getty Images; **7**r ErikaMitchell/iStock/Getty Images

CHAPTER 2
9 Hulton Archive/Getty Images; **15** ilbusca/Digital Vision Vectors/Getty Images

CHAPTER 3
19 ilbusca/Digital Vision Vectors/Getty Images; **23** dlerick /iStock/Getty Images

CHAPTER 4
25 FactoryTh/iStock/Getty Images; **28** stockcreations /Shutterstock.com

CHAPTER 5
33 Rawpixel/iStock/Getty Images; **37** Haitong Yu/Moment /Getty Images; **40** © NOAO/AURA/NSF/SCIENCE SOURCE

CHAPTER 6
45 Dan Reynolds Photography/Moment/Getty Images; **47** Spiral Periodic Table by Robert W Harrison/Wikimedia Commons/ CC By-SA 3.0

CHAPTER 7
57 Archive Photos/Moviepix/Getty Images

CHAPTER 8
63 Salvator Barki/Moment/Getty Images; **69** zf L/Moment /Getty Images

CHAPTER 9
77 Artranq/iStock/Getty Images

CHAPTER 10
85 Jack Andersen/Photodisc/Getty Images; **89**l DedMityay /iStock/Getty Images; **89**r Andrew Brookes/Cultura/Getty Images

CHAPTER 11
93 AROON PHUKEED/Moment/Getty Images; **99** ilbusca /Digital Vision Vectors/Getty Images

CHAPTER 12
107 by wildestanimal/Moment/Getty Images; **111** Stephen Frink Collection / Alamy Stock Photo

CHAPTER 13
119 R.M. Nunes/Shutterstock.com; **120** MarcelC/iStock /Getty Images; **123** Robert McGouey/Wildlife / Alamy Stock Photo

CHAPTER 14
133 Georgette Douwma/Stone/Getty Images; **137** weiXx /iStock/Getty Images; **138** sciencephotos / Alamy Stock Photo

CHAPTER 15
149 Vasko/E+/Getty Images; **155** unkas_photo/iStock /Getty Images

CHAPTER 16
157 peepo/E+/Getty Images; **163** Nik_Merkulov/iStock /Getty Images

CHAPTER 17
169 PetrePlesea/E+/Getty Images; **171** Africa Studio /Shutterstock.com

CHAPTER 18
175 voloshin311/Shutterstock.com; **181** Lydia Vero /Shutterstock.com

CHAPTER 19
187t Lebazele/iStock/Getty Images; **187**b Universal History Archive/Universal Images Group/Getty Images

CHAPTER 20

199 OksanaKiian/iStock/Getty Images; **203** DG Stock
/Shutterstock.com

CHAPTER 21

207 Anjelika Gretskaia/Moment/Getty Images;
213 mikroman6/Moment/Getty Images

CHAPTER 22

217 John Parrot/Stocktrek Images/Getty Images;
225 Margarita Balashova/iStock/Getty Images

BACK MATTER

231 baona/E+/Getty Images; **233** (beaker) choness
/iStock/Getty images; **233, 237**b (burner) mozcann/E+
/Getty Images; **233** (burette) © Charles D. Winters/SCIENCE
SOURCE; **233** (burette clamp) Rabbitmindphoto/Shutter-
stock.com; **233** (clay triangle) Sara Sadler/Alamy Stock
Photo; **233** (crucible tongs) Betka82/iStock/Getty Images;
233 (crucible and cover) Rabbitmindphoto/Shutterstock
.com; **233** (disposable pipette) Paket/iStock/Getty Images;
233 (Erlenmeyer flask) choness/iStock/Getty images; **233**
(evaporating dish) rrocio/iStock/Getty Images; **233** (filter
funnel) mozcann/E+/Getty Images; **233** (filter paper)
© SCIENCE PHOTO LIBRARY/SCIENCE SOURCE; **234** (graduated cylinder) prill/iStock/Getty Images; **234** (hot plate)
Rabbitmindphoto/Shutterstock.com; **234** (iron ring)
Rabbitmindphoto/Shutterstock.com; **234** (electronic
laboratory balance) Martin Shields/Alamy Stock Photo;
234, 236 (triple beam laboratory balance) Science Photo
Library/Getty Images; **234** (mortar and pestle) Steven
Raniszewski/ Getty Images; **234** (pinchcock clamp) Photo
used with permission from United Scientific Supplies, Inc.;
234 (pipette and bulb) sciencephotos/Alamy Stock Photo;
234 (ring stand) nipastock/iStock/Getty Images; **234**
(safety goggles) Liudmyla Liudmyla/iStock/Getty Images;
234 (spatula) Anak Surasarang/Shutterstock.com; **234** (stirring rod) Paday/iStock/Getty Images; **235** (test tube clamp)
Rabbitmindphoto/Shutterstock.com; **235** (test tubes)
Nicholas Shkoda/iStock/Getty Images; **235** (wash bottle)
© Turtle Rock Scientific/SCIENCE SOURCE; **235** (watch
glass) Chadchai Krisadapong/iStock/Getty Images; **235**
(weighing paper) Sarah Lompe; **235** (wire gauze) © Martyn
F. Chillmaid/SCIENCE SOURCE; **236**b Martin Shields/Alamy
Stock Photo; **237**t Martin Shields/Alamy Stock Photo; **242**
kali9/E+/Getty Images

Periodic Table
OF THE ELEMENTS

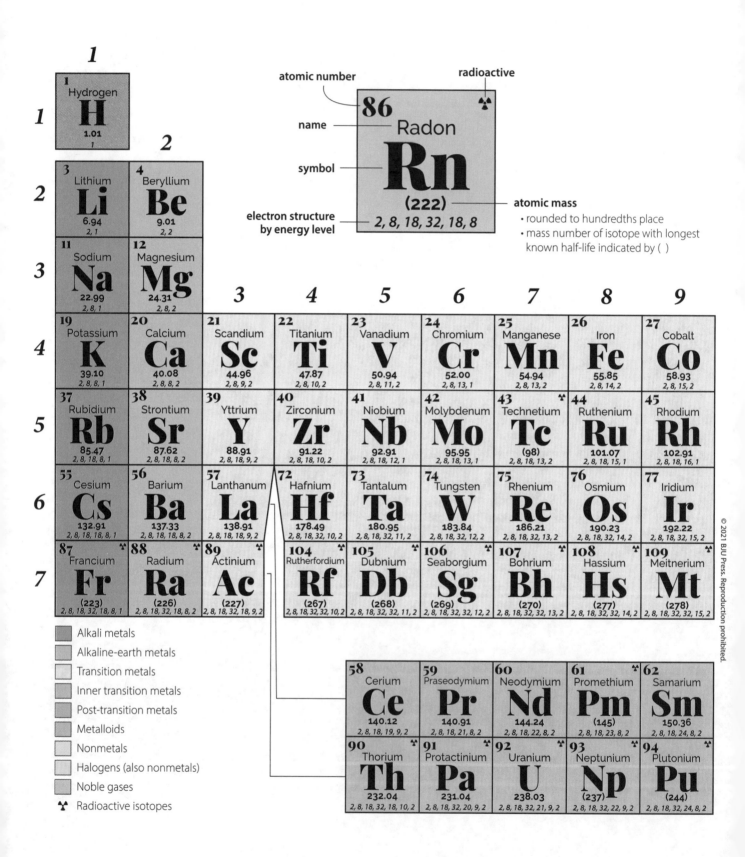

Legend

- Alkali metals
- Alkaline-earth metals
- Transition metals
- Inner transition metals
- Post-transition metals
- Metalloids
- Nonmetals
- Halogens (also nonmetals)
- Noble gases
- ☢ Radioactive isotopes

Key (Radon example)
- atomic number: 86
- name: Radon
- symbol: Rn
- atomic mass: (222)
- electron structure by energy level: 2, 8, 18, 32, 18, 8
- radioactive ☢
- atomic mass
  - rounded to hundredths place
  - mass number of isotope with longest known half-life indicated by ( )

18

| 2 | Helium | **He** | 4.00 | 2 |

13 **14** **15** **16** **17**

| 5 Boron **B** 10.81 2, 3 | 6 Carbon **C** 12.01 2, 4 | 7 Nitrogen **N** 14.01 2, 5 | 8 Oxygen **O** 16.00 2, 6 | 9 Fluorine **F** 19.00 2, 7 | 10 Neon **Ne** 20.18 2, 8 |
| 13 Aluminum **Al** 26.98 2, 8, 3 | 14 Silicon **Si** 28.09 2, 8, 4 | 15 Phosphorus **P** 30.97 2, 8, 5 | 16 Sulfur **S** 32.06 2, 8, 6 | 17 Chlorine **Cl** 35.45 2, 8, 7 | 18 Argon **Ar** 39.95 2, 8, 8 |

10 **11** **12**

28 Nickel **Ni** 58.69 2, 8, 17, 1	29 Copper **Cu** 63.55 2, 8, 18, 1	30 Zinc **Zn** 65.38 2, 8, 18, 2	31 Gallium **Ga** 69.72 2, 8, 18, 3	32 Germanium **Ge** 72.63 2, 8, 18, 4	33 Arsenic **As** 74.92 2, 8, 18, 5	34 Selenium **Se** 78.97 2, 8, 18, 6	35 Bromine **Br** 79.90 2, 8, 18, 7	36 Krypton **Kr** 83.80 2, 8, 18, 8
46 Palladium **Pd** 106.42 2, 8, 18, 18	47 Silver **Ag** 107.87 2, 8, 18, 1	48 Cadmium **Cd** 112.41 2, 8, 18, 18, 2	49 Indium **In** 114.82 2, 8, 18, 18, 3	50 Tin **Sn** 118.71 2, 8, 18, 18, 4	51 Antimony **Sb** 121.76 2, 8, 18, 18, 5	52 Tellurium **Te** 127.60 2, 8, 18, 18, 6	53 Iodine **I** 126.90 2, 8, 18, 18, 7	54 Xenon **Xe** 131.29 2, 8, 18, 18, 8
78 Platinum **Pt** 195.08 2, 8, 18, 32, 17, 1	79 Gold **Au** 196.97 2, 8, 18, 32, 18, 1	80 Mercury **Hg** 200.59 2, 8, 18, 32, 18, 2	81 Thallium **Tl** 204.38 2, 8, 18, 32, 18, 3	82 Lead **Pb** 207.2 2, 8, 18, 32, 18, 4	83 Bismuth **Bi** 208.98 2, 8, 18, 32, 18, 5	84 Polonium **Po** (209) 2, 8, 18, 32, 18, 6	85 Astatine **At** (210) 2, 8, 18, 32, 18, 7	86 Radon **Rn** (222) 2, 8, 18, 32, 18, 8
110 Darmstadtium **Ds** (281) 2, 8, 18, 32, 32, 17, 1	111 Roentgenium **Rg** (282) 2, 8, 18, 32, 32, 17, 2	112 Copernicium **Cn** (285) 2, 8, 18, 32, 32, 18, 2	113 Nihonium **Nh** (286) 2, 8, 18, 32, 32, 18, 3	114 Flerovium **Fl** (289) 2, 8, 18, 32, 32, 18, 4	115 Moscovium **Mc** (290) 2, 8, 18, 32, 32, 18, 5	116 Livermorium **Lv** (293) 2, 8, 18, 32, 32, 18, 6	117 Tennessine **Ts** (294) 2, 8, 18, 32, 32, 18, 7	118 Oganesson **Og** (294) 2, 8, 18, 32, 32, 18, 8

| 63 Europium **Eu** 151.96 2, 8, 18, 25, 8, 2 | 64 Gadolinium **Gd** 157.25 2, 8, 18, 25, 9, 2 | 65 Terbium **Tb** 158.93 2, 8, 18, 27, 8, 2 | 66 Dysprosium **Dy** 162.50 2, 8, 18, 28, 8, 2 | 67 Holmium **Ho** 164.93 2, 8, 18, 29, 8, 2 | 68 Erbium **Er** 167.26 2, 8, 18, 30, 8, 2 | 69 Thulium **Tm** 168.93 2, 8, 18, 31, 8, 2 | 70 Ytterbium **Yb** 173.05 2, 8, 18, 32, 8, 2 | 71 Lutetium **Lu** 174.97 2, 8, 18, 32, 9, 2 |
| 95 Americium **Am** (243) 2, 8, 18, 32, 25, 8, 2 | 96 Curium **Cm** (247) 2, 8, 18, 32, 25, 9, 2 | 97 Berkelium **Bk** (247) 2, 8, 18, 32, 27, 8, 2 | 98 Californium **Cf** (251) 2, 8, 18, 32, 28, 8, 2 | 99 Einsteinium **Es** (252) 2, 8, 18, 32, 29, 8, 2 | 100 Fermium **Fm** (257) 2, 8, 18, 32, 30, 8, 2 | 101 Mendelevium **Md** (258) 2, 8, 18, 32, 31, 8, 2 | 102 Nobelium **No** (259) 2, 8, 18, 32, 32, 8, 2 | 103 Lawrencium **Lr** (266) 2, 8, 18, 32, 32, 8, 3 |